CW01021754

OWN DE BEAU VOIR!

Jonathan Hoskins

*Fiction
**Non-fiction

JOURNAL*

7

RELATED ACCOUNTS**

199

APPENDICES**

293

JOURNAL

Transcriber's Note

The text conforms to the format of a personal journal, and all the evidence suggests it is exactly that. The manuscript was recovered from the author's home shortly after the date of its final entry. It is clearly bespoke and it is poorly fabricated. The stitching is extremely loose and this has allowed the author to insert several dozen images and separate sheets of notes throughout. Each is reproduced here at the point it was found inserted, in relation to the main text of the journal. A great deal of work has been done to identify them, and this information accompanies each one.

The original script features several typographical markings, recurrently. Asterisks are used for notes and marginalia. In the manuscript, the referent notes are not located in relation to the main body text with any regularity. Each one has been inserted where it was judged to be of best use to the reader. Most follow the referring asterisk, though where this would have been disruptive, it comes at the end of the paragraph, or even at the very end of that journal entry.

There are many words struck through, and many improper capitalisations. It is rarely clear whether these are corrections, a means of indexing, or editing for some other purpose. Because of this uncertainty, they have all been reproduced as they appear in the original manuscript, though made uniform for the sake of intelligibility. A small number of the entries are more anomalous, tangential or incomprehensible and these have been omitted.

J.H.

Anything begins when it is set in motion. And so
it is: this morning, I went for a walk.

First north, but newly installed over the
trees, there are cranes: great lengths of trussing,
pointing out awkward angles. All disordered.
(No one needs to see that in the morning.)

An about-turn south along Stamford and
already, from here, a **BARNACLE** visible,
affixed to the furniture beside the eucalyptus.
A barnacle, but like everything: deliberate.
A notice!

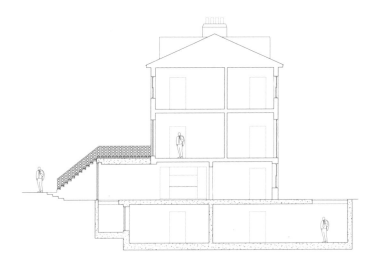

The eucalyptus owners propose to extend
their home to a fourth storey – by displacing all
of the material for **FOUR METRES** beneath it.

My immediate concern is for the foundations of these homes, which is only a skin of lime over the Gravels, before the first course of brick.

This has implications. Something has been set in motion. I will have to look into it some more.

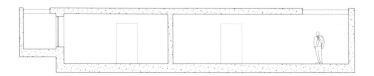

(Afterthought: as I was taking down the details, a man stopped to do the same. I know this man. Or at least, I know his lurcher. He began to tell me what it "would mean for the area". Realising, only now: I have no recollection of what he said thereafter. The way he used that term, "the area". Also only now: the conversation beyond that first point was entirely conditional upon my passing an EXAMINATION I wasn't even aware of sitting. I took 'the Area' (UNTHINKINGLY) as shorthand for the special status ~~geographically~~ volumetrically* identical with De Beauvoir, the AREA OF CONSERVATION, and responded accordingly, to his obvious satisfaction. I had managed to respond as this man had demanded without realising it.)

*If there's one thing this morning reminds, it's that De Beauvoir is a volume and not an Area, at all.

Planning application (elevation). Date unknown.

7TH JUNE 2005

The extraction plans continue to cause bother, and it is because I cannot see exactly why they do so.

The plans, if carried through, will force upon the Area a novel MUTABILITY. They prescribe the removal of all material for four metres beneath the entire footprint of the house, amounting to at least the volume of a typical outbuilding of the Area.

It could be OBJECTED that those outbuildings are themselves the effects of a comparable DISPLACEMENT of material from the Area, because they ~~comprise~~ are assembled from London Stock that was dug from (and indeed, fired in) the Area itself.

But therein is the difference. In the current example, but not in the historical one, there is an offence to the sum constitution of the Area, to the indivisible whole. When these 200 cubic metres are removed over the coming months, removed they shall be – from the Area entirely.

The loss will be irretrievable.

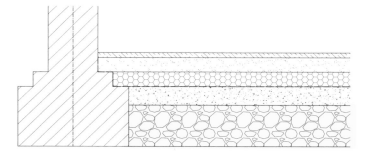

The eucalyptus owners must be new to the Area. They will need to be told.

De Beauvoir Town. c.1973
Planning application (cross-sectional elevation). Date unknown.
Brick manufacture on Beauvoir Estate. c.1800

(Draft)

TO WHOM IT MAY CONCERN,

WELCOME TO THE AREA!

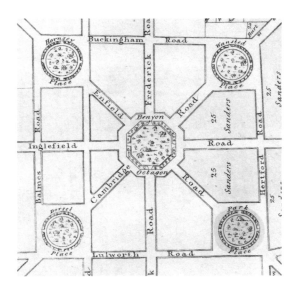

SOME OTHERS AMONG YOUR NEW FELLOW CONSTITUENTS WILL RECOUNT TO YOU THE FOLLOWING, IN TIME, I AM SURE. I CAN SEE THAT NONE HAVE ALREADY, AND THAT HAS BROUGHT ABOUT A TERRIBLE DANGER. PLEASE ALLOW ME TO EXPLAIN.

THE AREA IS THE PROUD CONSEQUENCE
OF TWO CENTURIES OF MATERIAL
ASSEMBLY. THIS ASSEMBLY SHOULD
HAVE OCCURRED IN ITS ENTIRETY AT
THE OUTSET, AND WITH AN ENTIRELY
HARMONIOUS SYMMETRY. BUT IT WAS
ARRESTED, MID-COMPLETION, AND
CONSEQUENTLY: MUTILATED! AS LATER
ILLUSTRATIONS REVEAL:

WITH THE SYMMETRY IRREVERSIBLY
ANNULLED, OUR PLANNED CONSTITUTION
WOULD BE, AS WELL.

THEREAFTER, THE SYMMETRY COULD NEVER BE ANYTHING BUT A FANCIFUL FICTION THAT EVERYONE OF THE AREA WOULD KNOW OF, BUT NEVER KNOW. THE CONSTITUTION WOULD BE COMPLETED IN TIME, BUT ONLY THROUGH TWO CENTURIES OF ~~COMMON~~ DELIBERATIVE ASSEMBLY.

(I CANNOT TELL YOU THE DETAIL OF THIS PERIOD, BUT IT IS SURELY CIRCUITOUS AND FUGACIOUS, BECAUSE THE CONSTITUTION REQUIRED ALMOST TWO CENTURIES TO BE COMPLETED. WHATEVER. IT ALL TOOK PLACE WITHIN THE AREA AND THIS IS THE ONLY DETAIL NECESSARY FOR ITS LEGITIMACY.)

IT IS A REMARKABLE HISTORY, BUT ONE THAT RENDERS THE MATERIAL CONSTITUTION OF THE AREA THE ONLY ONE IN EXISTENCE, OF ANY KIND – THERE IS NO PLAN THAT IT CORRESPONDS TO, BECAUSE THE DELIBERATORS HAD NO CHOICE BUT TO PROCEED WITHOUT ONE. IN TIME, THEY ASSEMBLED A CONSTITUTION THAT IS BEYOND ANY PLAN: IT IS ITS OWN PLAN, THE ONLY RECORD OF ITSELF, HANGING TOGETHER AS ONE.

THIS IS WHY IT IS SUCH AN OFFENCE FOR ANY VOLUME OF IT TO BE CLEAVED AND DISCARDED IN ANOTHER PLACE.

I TRUST YOU WILL ABANDON YOUR PROPOSED EXCAVATION.

YOURS ~~CONSTITUTIVELY~~ CONSTITUTIONALLY.

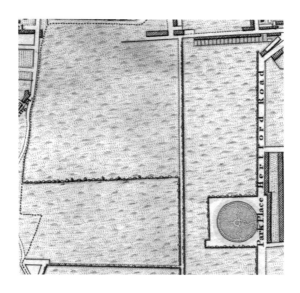

Plan for Beauvoir Town Estate. 1821
Weller's map of London. 1868
Greenwood map of London. 1826

ADDENDUM: the offence of the proposed Excavation is TWOFOLD. The first offence stands as before: the wilful amputation of a part of the Constitution. The second follows from the first.

To reason:

The Constitution was assembled by procedures of DELIBERATION, and completed in only the most recent living memory. This should not have been necessary – it once had a plan but it DIVERGED from this plotted path. But: today that divergence affords our Constitution a total transparency. In other areas, a Constitution can be found in a library. Not here. It is always accessible; if it were not, we would have neither roofs to keep the rain out, nor walls to hold them up. But in so remaining accessible, our Constitution is always and perfectly vulnerable. At any moment, any part of it can be abused* [*better put: EXTRACTED]. The Area is singular, and the disfigurement of a PART is a disfigurement of the WHOLE.

It cannot be policed at every point, at every instant. But remain intact, it does. Each moment the Constitution remains intact is a moment it is UPHELD, a moment of every Constituent demonstrably honouring his commitment to all others, to see it sustained. The Constitution is VULNERABLE, always, but always it is left alone, upheld. The Stock forever weathers, but the Constitution is RENEWED in every moment the Area remains unchanged by all of the Constituents.

The Area is so-called because it has been AUTHORISED to have this special status. But an Authoriser will take up any such invitation. And in any case: to give this any regard is to put the cart before the horse:

    i. The Constitution cannot be Authorised at every point and in every moment.

    ii. Thus: some other force must be responsible for it remaining so demonstrably intact (at every point and in every moment).

    iii. Thus: this force can only be the SINCERE OBLIGATION of each Constituent towards all others, expressed through the Constitution.

This obligation has been ~~met with resistance~~ BETRAYED. The implications are still beyond me, but the most immediate danger is to Constitutional obligation. The proposal introduces a contagion to us all, to the sound of: "Among whom else is obligation failing?"

This evening I scoured the Area for notices of the Excavation and removed them all. No one can know there is anything the matter.

Corner of Ufton Road and Downham Road. 1973

10TH JUNE 2005

The first signs are here.

There is NEW ASSEMBLY along Culford Mews, as I have seen with my own eyes, this morning. Worse still, it is a length of razor wire, scalpel sharp. There is only ever one reason to install razor wire: FEAR OF TRESPASS. And there is only one reason to fear trespass: fear for the commitment of common Constituents.

This is how it begins.

The Excavation is a patent, extraordinary ~~affront~~ displacement of a part of the Constitution, but I realise only now the scale of resources that must have been propelling it, and the degree of contempt for the Constitution that it represents.
   Urgency must rest with ~~securing~~ ~~salvaging~~ TRANSFERRING the Constitution into some other form – a RECONSTITUTION. In being so transferred, the Constitution will become immutable, and immune to the deleteriousness (lit.) of the Extraction. The Constitution will be restored, but not before a necessary period of quarantine. This threat has momentum for now, but time will show it to be only transient. It will ~~give way~~ subside.* [*Subsidence!] In the meantime, the Constitution will have a very different existence, or it will have none at all.

De Beauvoir Town. c.1975

11TH JUNE 2005

Reconstitution begins: an exhaustive, descriptive account of the Area. It is the most suitable ~~mutation~~ VEHICLE for transference because it disallows any pretensions to Reconstitution in and of itself. Patently, that will only occur in the mind of the READER. This is the DEVICE that will protect the Constitution from aggressors during its period of quarantine.*

*"Manuscripts don't burn."

13TH JUNE 2005

Text has been proven inappropriate as a vehicle for Reconstitution. After many thousands of words it has scarcely got to the front gate, but that is not the problem. The problem is this: when the Assembly is Reconstituted in the mind, it is ANEW. It bears no relation to the Constitution. It is aside from it; apart. My project is to SECURE the Constitution, not to SUCCEED it! Another approach.

7TH JULY 2005

RECONSTITUTION:
(2nd draft)

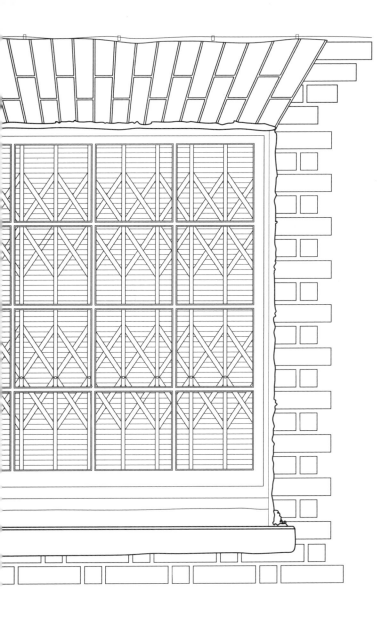

Author's studies. Date unknown.

11TH JULY 2005

The second draft ~~errs wants~~ BOTHERS.
There were good reasons for not pursuing it
in the first instance. These still stand, but
now alongside another.

Yesterday, completing a study: a man
walks by – starts to speak, in ADMIRATION.
As he goes on, it is clear: his admiration is
not projected towards me, and not towards
my study, and not even towards my object,
the referent, a rubbed brick lintel, atop
symmetrically bevelled glazing bars and
panels, all from the earliest years of Assembly.

No: as this man spoke, his words
drew relation with only the ~~exterior visible~~
EPIDERMIS of my object, as if that – the
appearance of the object on this day, as he
had chanced to walk past this spot – had been
created *ex nihilo*. Talk of LINE, LIGHT and
FINISH, only. Worse, he seemed to be inviting
a common moment between the two of us. Not
only had he assumed that I admired only the
epidermis, as he did, but he deduced it from
my ACTIVITY.

Logically, I can dismiss this. (I have never seen
this man before. I doubt he is of the Area.)
Intuitively, I am ambivalent.

14TH JULY 2005

I have found a stain.

The sheets had been on my desk all morning and I had obviously set a mug down upon them, not cognising ~~their significance~~ the significance I supposed for them.

Upsetting, in itself – but far more troubling to realise, minutes later, that I could still see NO SIGNIFICANCE in this sheet. I leafed through all of the studies in turn. Each one forced the same acknowledgement.

The Constitution is NOWHERE in these images. It's not the loss that comes with transferring three dimensions into two. It's not even the loss of the original material. From these drawings, with material appropriated from the Area (fate forbid), a competent facsimile of the original objects could be produced. But: they would be without a grain of the Constitution. The Deliberative means of Assembly will have been lost.

(After some hours: the phenomenon is rather like the realisation that one has misread the scale of a map. The distance to travel is suddenly many times greater; the spans to cross, many times broader; and the dominance of one's own path over and against its surroundings, already precarious, diminishes to become almost imperceptible.)

Author's study. Date unknown.

20TH JULY 2005

THE DAILY LAMENT FOR THE SYMMETRY.

Passed this afternoon:

A front garden birdfeeder, askew.

Birds compensating; feed trailing to one corner of the dish.

Land animals, wise enough to know: disturbing the post brings the (g)rain.

The Constituent has tried to secure the feed for the birds by re-Assembling the post, but it has failed. She has tried to secure the post, to secure the feed, by erecting a shallow barrier* [*hoarding?] around it, but this has failed. The grain, carried away by all and any.

How completed it is; how complete it could have been!

I would not, under any normal circumstances, say that I LIVE IN the Area. I would say that I am OF the Area. But both statements are true, and this is a rare moment when the first seems more appropriate.

It is because I am IN the Area that I have no need – that I have NEVER had any need – to go in search of the Deliberation that it was Assembled from. It is aggregated all around me, at every moment. We, the Constituents, are its intimate BENEFICIARIES. Circumstances now demand that my understanding of its history becomes ~~exacting~~ COMPREHENSIVE, and very quickly so.

But it is a time of CONSTITUTIONAL CRISIS – not only an existential threat, but one that no experience has prepared us to contain.

I know of only one place where even some of this Deliberation may already be convened.

MILITANT MUMS DEMAND ACTION NOW

Battle

op lady Mrs Hubbard
down in Balls Pond
, a series of demos
sed to get a proper
th lights outside De
hool. Mrs Hubbard
this blow by blow
the demos to help the
campaigners.

wrote to the Isling-
. We never heard from
so we decided to have
tion. In doing so we
Balls Pond Rd by the
warned the council
our demonstration
ummer holidays.
emonstration was on
and this was a great
he drivers did not
ad happened and this
urprise to them.

New Town tenants are in a mili-
tant mood over the experimental
road closures and a Tenants'
Action Group headed by Emilie
Chalk has been formed to make
their voices heard above the
roar of traffic thundering along
Downham Road.

As we were going to press, the
action group announced plans for
demos on June 13 and 14 to close
the junction of Downham and De
Beauvoir roads.

The impact of the closures has
been to make them feel cut off
and abandoned and they want
Downham and De Beauvoir roads
closed before a child dies. If
the council won't agree to this,
they will demand the immediate
reopening of Northchurch, Hertford and Enfield roads.

Backed by worried mothers, Mrs
Chalk of Trinity Court, has been
collecting thousands of signa-
tures for a petition protesting
that the closures have made some
roads more dangerous than ever
for their children.

DBA chairman Graham Parsey
pledged support for the closure
of Downham and De Beauvoir roads
but warned: "The battle is turning into an Old versus New Town,
must fight what the GLC wants. We
pressure is built up we can get
something done when the six
months is up."

Mums' chorus: "We can't wait six months."
"Take the barricades down now!"
"All these committees are no
good. We'll close roads ourselves and chop down the barriers!"

*this make sure it is
time of the day, and
ected as the police
cials will divert
. Never let them know
else you are left*

We want a play space but we can't cross the road.

If you are wondering wha
pened from Jan 70 - Apri
READ ON:

1970   Central GIA set
advisory ctte of
residents

June 71   Ctte put forward
for closures thr
town

Oct 71   2 representative
each affected ar
demand on residen

Nov 71   DBA demand closu

Downham Rd in SA
report to council

Jan 72   Proposals for ce
area go on publi
bition.

Feb 72   Residents Ctte a
findings of exhi
and meeting

Mar - May 72 Environment
prepared environ
report

June 72   Report approved
dents Ctte

July 72   Report submitted
council

Dec 72   Report approved

B De eaver

No 28   APRIL 1977

SOUTHGATE
GROVE

UFTON ROAD

No 1

Sitting Area

Sitting Area I

Venture Play 3

Sunken Ball Area 4

PARKWAY

DOWNHAM ROAD

New Pelic

2 Dorleston

UFTON RD CENTRE & MINI-PAR

AT LAST

BY THIS TIME next year De Beauvoir
will have a new park.

Hackney Council at its meeting on
January 26th finally approved the
imaginative scheme for the vacant
factory (Cydax) at No 12 Ufton Rd
to be repaired and used by the

outside and insi
3 An Adventure Par
paid leaders thr
linked with one
provide covered
winter and wet w
4 A sunken ball g
lighting to allo

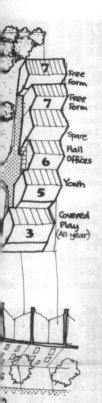

Free
form

7

Free
Form

Spare

7

Hall
Offices

6

Youth

5

Covered
Play
(All year)

3

Local resident Crispin Aubrey with da

T'S OURS

children run by
the year
the factory to
ilities in

a with flood-
en to have a

to hear the views of the immediate
neighbours 'We are not against the
scheme, but we need reassurances
that adequate security, supervision
and restrictions on hours are provided.'

April start

The clearance of the site will
start in April and the repairs to

PUBLISHED BY J KOTZ   Agent 103 SHEPHERDESS WALK LONDON N 1

it was supposed to have been very pretty. It's very run down and it needs sprucing up. When no homes are built they should be small compact flats. De Beauvoir needs no more high rise flats. De Beauvoir needs looking after.

Children played in safety behind this road block of banners when members of De Beauvoir Association Committee organised a demo in Tottenham Road to show their concern at the needless demolition of housing and the determination of IILEA to ignore the benefits of expanding north over Tottenham Road onto derelict land, owned by Whitbread's, which has been derelict for years, was miraculously rolled and smartly aspected within three days of the demo. An attempt to steamroller the opposition?

LETTERS: on road-naming

[Inserted page]

FIRST BULLETIN (1):
May 1971

FREQUENCY:
~~Alternate months~~ ~~Three annually~~ Variable.

DELIBERATORS:
~~Doris Kibblewhite~~
~~Stuart Weir~~
~~Robin Young~~
~~Frank Fletcher~~
~~Reg Crowfoot~~
~~William Verity~~
~~Joan Childs~~
~~Adrian Dobson~~
~~M Young~~
~~Mrs du Sautoy~~
~~Eric Laws~~
~~Ron Adamson~~
~~Joe Bray~~
~~Mabel Hall~~
~~Mrs Machin~~
~~Mrs Parrott~~
~~Mr Paveley~~
~~Mrs Paveley~~

(TOO MANY TO CATALOGUE.)

De Beaver newsletter 16. 1974
De Beaver newsletter 28. 1977
De Beaver newsletter 15. 1974

MUMS' TAKE

A group of mothers are seeking to take over the house formerly occupied by the

council might decide to re for commercial or industri

OVER BID

house

PHOTO HACKNEY GAZETTE

...need expressed by residents of the southern area and ...the New Town.

These protesting pupils from Edith Cavell school were among 400 who recently held a day's strike & marched to ILEA's divisional office – backed by their parents and teachers. They handed in a petition protesting against the proposed closure of the school in 1980. A couple of marshals on the march were approached by an ex-chairman of the Old Cavellians who has since contacted 350 former pupils. He is going to organise a protest meeting. Mrs Irene Lane, secretary of the Parent-Teacher Association, is also organising a follow-up meeting at the lower school.

repair. Almost without exception, they have bulging walls, uneven settlement, bad rising damp, leaking roofs & completely rotted mortar. Young is now negotiating with owners to find out who will carry out works themselves and who can't afford to. The Trust is willing to rehouse both owners and tenants

Local people may have raised their eyebrows when they saw workmen in 3 houses which have been empty, abandoned and bordering on dereliction for years — 30 Englefield Rd, 105 Tottenham and 125 Culford. Hackney Council owned these houses and agreed to sell them (& 123 Tottenham Rd, which was part-occupied) to the De Beauvoir Trust in February 1969.

It was August 1969 before the Trust got permission to survey them. It was August 1970 before the Council fixed a price for them — and by then vandalism and decay made it necessary for the Trust to survey the houses again.

It was February 1971 before the Council settled the

well with official valuations c
given when the terrace was not
But the Trust's initiative to s
houses and to allow residents t
in them can be wrecked by one o
ish owner.

LONDON by I

Felix Haslett, who is 90, live
He is really a Clerkenwell man
only lived in De Beauvoir for
driver, he has driven all over
all over London. Here, with hi
one of the poems he writes:

May I say, Friends, these litt
notions of the contemporary so
things I have been acquainted
days to the present. They are
abridged versions with a sort
gerel. This is my opinion abou
aliens and strangers:

I've walked through London str
I've traversed many a mile.
I scan the faces as they pass

Only the very young are gay.
This merry mood soon fades awa

[Inserted page]

POINTS OF ASSEMBLY:
- TOTTENHAM ROAD (JUNCTION WITH CULFORD ROAD)
- PICONS (BASIN)
- 45 DE BEAUVOIR ROAD
- NORTHCHURCH TERRACE (ALL)
- TOTTENHAM ROAD (BETWEEN CULFORD AND DE BEAUVOIR ROAD)
- ENFIELD ROAD (EDITH CAVELL?)
- 169 DE BEAUVOIR ROAD
- 57 DE BEAUVOIR ROAD
- 2 DE BEAUVOIR SQUARE
- HERTFORD ROAD (JUNCTION WITH DOWNHAM ROAD)
- ENGLEFIELD ROAD (JUNCTION WITH SOUTHGATE ROAD)
- ST PETERS CHURCH (CRYPT)
- 11-12 DE BEAUVOIR SQUARE

POINTS OF ASSEMBLY (REVISED):
TAXI RANKS IN FILE. EVERY DAY THERE SEEM TO BE ABOUT 30 TAXIS PARKED IN CULFORD & TOTTENHAM ROADS NEAR WHERE THE NEW SCHOOL IS BEING BUILT. LOCAL PEOPLE CAN'T PARK THEIR CARS NEAR THEIR HOUSES. SURELY THE ROAD IS NOT SUPPOSED TO BE USED AS PRIVATE PARKING AND GARAGING FOR A PRIVATE TAXI FIRM? MRS M.B., CULFORD ROAD, N1

MICHAEL'S GENERAL STORE 2 BUCKINGHAM ROAD OPEN 8-8.30 6 DAYS

A WEEK EARLY CLOSING WEDNESDAY
SUNDAY 9-2 4-8.30 SWEETS – CIGS –
ICE CREAMS – ALL FROZEN FOODS –
PROVISIONS – STATIONERY AND TOILET
GOODS

HIDE PARK? THE DE BEAUVOIR SQUARE
GARDENS ARE BEAUTIFULLY KEPT AND
WOULD EVEN BE MORE PLEASANT IF
THERE WERE SHRUBS PLANTED ALONG
THE INSIDE RAILINGS, WHICH WOULD
PARTLY HIDE THE STREET AND MAKE IT A
REAL GARDEN ENCLOSURE. MRS H WALD
114 CULFORD RD

THERE ARE STILL REAL DIFFICULTIES:
1) THE NEED TO MAKE THE AUTHORITIES
   TREAT THE AREA AS A WHOLE;
2) PRESSURE OF WINKLING ON TENANTS
   & HOUSE PRICES; 3) LACK OF CONTROL
   OF INDUSTRIAL NUISANCES LIKE PICONS.

WHAT PROTECTION DO THE TENANTS
HAVE? FIRST, AN UNFURNISHED TENANT
HAS AN ALMOST ABSOLUTE RIGHT TO
STAY ON IN HIS HOME. THE LANDLORD
MUST THEN GO TO COUNTY COURT TO
ASK FOR AN ORDER FOR

(TOO MANY TO CATALOGUE.)

De Beaver newsletter 18. 1974
De Beaver newsletter 9. 1972
De Beaver newsletter 4. 1971

NGUI'S
ATE
AD

" said Graham Parsey
ial meeting in Oct-
leader Martin Otto-
b Masters, with a
ident representa-
had been called to
three year effort
nt factory at No 12
munity use.

was covered in De
ago as September 74-
ll-year covered play
the adventure park,
youth activities,
term a sports hall,
centre for local
complementary act-
rby Rose Lipman
will form part of
park which will be
vacant former pre-
unction of Ufton and
couple of years

confirmed that since
not seeking any an-

CABARET
LIVE AT LIPMAN

NICK ON STAGE   photo: ROGER PERRY

NICK EDMETT, the fast rising cabaret
star, has been booked for December
18th at the Rose Lipman, for the
CANDLELIGHT CABARET PARTY (Tickets
£1.50, all proceeds towards the
Ufton Road Factory Project and the
Adventure Playground).

We went to see his show at the Tram-
shed in Woolwich, with Doris and Peter
Kibblewhite, and had a smashing evening. He danced and sang and tore the
heart-strings not only from Marlene,
as seen above (yes, there is a beard
as well) but also from Kipling and
Shakespeare. He was backed up by an
excellent variety of singing acts.

S
C

PETE

PETER
came t
to ope
the ne
at the
the li

He har
tenant
their
Amanda
local
ton Da
ers he
DEL
After
Howett

ORE: `KEEP MMUNITIES'

photo: GRAHAM PARSEY

E GREETS THE HOWETTS

vironment Minister,
voir on November 17th
Mortimer Road, one of
system-built houses
f Englefield Road where
d to stand.

the keys to the new
and Doreen Howett and
Debra, Diana and
remony attended by
Brown and Stanley Clin-
Mayor and Council lead-
artin Ottolangui.

on the housing list the
lighted with their new

PRESERVE THE STREET

"The days of the bulldozer are over,"
he said. "In the community life of Inner London, the street has played as
important a part as the village has
in rural life. I think we do now recognise the importance of preserving
the street and preserving what people
know and understand."

Whilst stressing that the earlier
schemes were right at the time, he
continued:"Most of us recognise that
the design of housing on these large
cleared sites was often ill-conceived
and that in going for tower blocks or
large block estates insufficient ac-

1. NO TO 'EXTENSIVE DEMOLITION'
2. 6 MONTHS FOR FINAL DECISION

MR CLAYTON THE INSPECTOR

Geoffrey Rippon, newly appointed Secretary of State for the Environment, has decided not to allow Hackney Council to cancel De Beauvoir's southern area General

quiry in March into Hackney's resolution to cancel the GIA, advised Mr Rippon not to approve the Council's resolution – but suggested that a part, or

[Inserted page]

POINTS OF DELIBERATION:
i.   INDUSTRIAL NUISANCE
ii.   VACANT PLOT
       (see also i)
iii.   VALUATION
       (see also i)
iv.   UNSIGHTLINESS (see also i, ii, iii)
v.   GENERAL IMPROVEMENT AREA
       (see also i, ii, iii, iv)
vi.   SUICIDE
       (see also ii, iv)
vii.   PLAYGROUP
       (see also ii)
viii. WELFARE ADVICE (?)
       (see also ii, iii, iv, v, vii)
ix.   ELECTRICAL SUPERMARKET
       (see also i, iv, v)
x.   THE NORTH LONDON LINE (?)
       (see also i, iii, iv)
xi.   DISASSEMBLY/REASSEMBLY
       (see also i, ii, iii, iv, v, vi, x)
xii.   WINKLING (?)
       (see also i, ii, iii, iv, v, vi, viii, ix, x, xi)
xiii. WEDDING PHOTOGRAPHY (?)
       (see also ii, iv, v, vii, viii, xi, xii)
xiv.   TRUST (?)
       (see also i, ii, iii, iv, v, vii, viii, ix, x, xii)

De Beaver newsletter 27. 1976
De Beaver newsletter 9. 1972

15TH AUGUST 2005

I have been sleeping very badly.

The bulletins have not helped as I had hoped.

They are a CACOPHONY.

I have torn and dismembered every one in my efforts to Reconstitute them, but the truth is obvious and inescapable. They are the MIRROR of Deliberation, only – they are not themselves Deliberative. Deliberation is the leading edge, and the bulletins only follow it. The meetings in the Crypt, or the Mitre, or the Talbot; the calls to action; the demonstrations; the jubilation – it all appears in the future tense and in the past tense, but never in the present. COMMENTARY, however, is always in the present – because that is what is going on in these bulletins!

Deliberators...

"are speaking to..."

"are sending..."

"wish to complain that..."

"are staying put".

But such observations are only symptoms of the greater problem they only announce. All of this Deliberation, all of this commentary, is of the same ~~intellect~~ ~~insight~~ ~~size~~ SCALE as I am.

My stride is no GREATER than theirs, and my horizon is no more DISTANT. When I am hailed to a meeting next week, it is the same distance in the future for me as it is for them. When I am told of Deliberation that is ongoing, I do not know it* [*its NATURE] any more than they do.

The bulletins make AUTHORIAL DEMANDS of me that can only amount to a distraction. My only concern is for Deliberative Assembly, and I must be oriented towards – and by – that, and not commentary of it.

Probably St Peter's Crypt, De Beauvoir Road. c.1972

A BREAKTHROUGH! (of a kind).*
[*of two kinds!]

If my ultimate task is akin to using a tool
to fashion an EDIFICE, then it has become
necessary to first learn how to fashion the
TOOL with which to fashion that edifice.

 The Constitution exists at the scale of
life, and the innumerable Deliberative voices
it aggregates are each equal in scale to
my own. This RATIO OF SCALE must be
SHIFTED in my favour if I am to be capable
of even casting off on this expedition.

 The beginning of this new, prior task
is to determine what QUALITIES this tool
should have, returning attention to the
material of the Area; that which it has been
ASSEMBLED from; the CLAY EARTH of
De Beauvoir that was dug, fired and inverted
to become its edifices.

 The Stock is a famously, detrimentally
POROUS brick. (We know this; back then,
our hand was forced!) WATER settles in its
crevices and evaporates, depositing SALTS.
These salts form CRYSTALS that grow
over time – so irresistibly that THE BRICK
ITSELF SUCCUMBS, breaking apart and
revealing a more weathered face.

What rate of decay would be possible if this process were rationalised? I have experimented, with many **SALT SOLUTIONS** – chlorides, sulphates, nitrates, carbonates. All, applied as **SAMPLES** to representative buildings along Downham, Northchurch, Buckingham and Tottenham. Now clear: the natural weathering process can be **ACCELERATED**, many times over.

This mechanism is of exactly the kind I need so **URGENTLY**. With only a skin's thickness removed from buildings, the ratio of scale between myself and the Area is ~~recalibrated considerably~~ **TRANSFORMED**.

Only the INTERLOPER will regret the loss of the epidermis! All COMMITTED CONSTITUENTS will see that sentiment as ABSURD. Remove one epidermal layer of the Stock and what is revealed? Another! And each one is celebrated, in succession, for the charming period surface it bestows.

House adjacent to General Improvement Area showhouse. 1972
General Improvement Area showhouse. 1972

[Inserted page]

(Draft)

GENERAL NOTICE:

FOR THE ATTENTION OF
EVERY PERSON OF THE AREA;

EVERY PERSON WHO HAS MADE
THE AREA THEIR OWN.

THIS NOTICE EXTENDS
THE INVITATION TO ALL:

TO HAVE EXECUTED UPON
YOUR EXTERIOR AN EXCEPTIONAL

'PERIOD CHARM WASH' (Bigger)

TO ELEVATE ITS NATURAL MATURITY
AND MATURE ITS NATURAL ELEVATION.

THE PERIOD CHARM WASH
WILL REMOVE THE UNKEMPT SURFACE
YOU KNOW, AND REVEAL THE HIDDEN
SPECTACLE YOU DON'T.

THIS IS MY CONTRIBUTION

TO THE CONTINUING ~~COMPLETENESS~~
INTEGRITY OF THE AREA.

(Contact)

24TH AUGUST 2005

The first 'Period Charm Wash' has been completed. I was ~~a bag of nerves~~ a little apprehensive.

I have tested the Solution well, but the Stock is everywhere inconsistent, and I am concerned for the efficacy it will have against each untested surface. My nerves surely showed, judging from my first client's generous adamant offers of help.*
[*An insistent assistant...]

The application needs refinement. Working at height, it is easy to see the Solution run off paving, patios and porches, and onto lawns, beds and garden furniture. I worry what effect this is having but there have been no complaints thus far. (It is all for the greater cause.)

This evening, the water has evaporated from my boots and both are left pocked with salt spots. If the same is true of the rest of my clothes (which it must be) then I have spent today, at the very least, successfully impregnating myself with an abrasive agent!*

[*I have sourced boiler suits in an appropriate pewter grey, in quantities that will outlast its corrosiveness over the many applications to come.]

BUT there is much to TAKE HEART from. The penetration was at least as pronounced as I had hoped. Close up, one can easily see the age of the Stock surface and the keying it offers the Solution.

The client stayed with me up to the very end of the application, even as the light began to fail – and waiting until this time to tell me she is soon to LEAVE THE AREA.

The SHOCK of hearing this! Only dulled with explanation. She will move to an island, ~~another~~ a small island, very far away. El Hierro – 'THE IRON'. Complete, and completely self-sustaining. A symmetry, of sorts: rising to a single point from a three-pointed base. An assembly of integral strength that is complete and self-reliant: the only appropriate home for any former Constituent.

COMPREHENDED

BY AID OF <u>THE SOLUTION</u>,
C.11TH NOVEMBER 2005

AND

ITS EFFECTS ON THE <u>RATIO OF SCALE</u>

BETWEEN <u>THE AREA</u> AND
<u>THE RECONSTITUENT</u>.

FOLLOWING <u>THE LOSS OF THE SYMMETRY</u>,

THE <u>DELIBERATIVE ASSEMBLY</u>
OF THE AREA OCCURRED IN
<u>FOUR IDENTIFIABLE PERIODS</u>,

EACH ONE A ~~REJECTION~~ ~~INGESTION~~
USURPATION OF THE LAST:

i. <u>INAUGURATION</u> (BY SPECULATION).

ii. <u>EXCLUSION</u> (BY DISARRANGEMENT).

iii. <u>MATURATION</u> (BY ASSOCIATION).

iv. <u>COMPLETION</u> (BY AUTHORISATION).

6TH SEPTEMBER 2005

It is ironic that, for all of my CONCERN over the Solution, and for all of my COMMITMENT to the Constitution, it is the latter that now brings more despondency to my days.

I try to introduce ROUTINE to the application whenever I can, but the Constitution REFUSES it. I will work between two windows, and the architrave to my left will be different to the one on my right. I will have more confidence before a booking adjacent to one previous, only to find the door casing entirely dissimilar, and the pointing in an altogether different state of repair.

A new strategy is needed for every client.

But, every time: PRESENT and PREVIOUS will be of the same moment of Assembly. (And that moment, I assume to be – from its dominance – the ~~origin~~ inauguration of the Area). Prompting the question: what kind of ALIEN DELIBERATION was then in operation?

This is the kind of Constituent we need to be concerned about. For it to be effective, the Solution must be applied Comprehensively. I am not able to choose my clients, and I am not able to choose my conversation.

"Have you travelled much?" (I did not bother to respond.) "Have you always lived in the Area?" (Again.)

Inside, as I worked, was a welcome distraction. DISTINCT through the sash panels: illustrations from all over. And artefacts. Alien script. I worry what kind of Constitution such people have (lit.!). Walls of gilded moulding, all a palm width in section, most an arm length in width, perhaps seven in total. All framing aerial illustrations, most familiar.

Very much fine detail. Most of it, imperceptible with the foreshortening, but some things would be visible from any distance.

In retrospect, showing an interest perhaps did no harm to securing a testimonial from this client. This one – much older than the others, at least by his account. But still very closely related to the Area (the scope of my concern clear by now?).

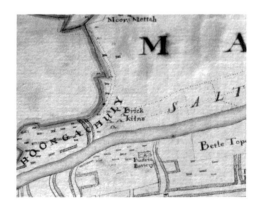

Besides the brick kilns? Yes, besides the brick kilns: it is "the origin of the Area, in a sense". In the sense of nonsense, presumably.

"The origins of the Benign ('Benion'?), and so, the origins of the Area."

I protested, finally, only to meet with refusal. "Truths are found in the nature of a thing – they are not imposed upon it." (I say it now: I have no idea what he meant by any of this.)

The Beauvoir and surrounding estates. c.1825
A Survey of the Town of Madraspatnam and the several Districts thereto belonging, and in possession of the Honourable United East India Company. 1733

To suppose, for a moment: what that man, that client, had to say was all accurate.

It would account for the most glaring contradiction in all of the Area's Deliberative Assembly: its commencement. How could Assembly proceed when there are no Deliberators? How could Deliberators proceed when there is no Assembly? When the Symmetry has been left mutilated and BEREFT?

Only with the most spectacular deployment of resources, the kind that can make SOMETHING of NOTHING. Resources gathered from around the globe, perhaps – like those of the Benign. A spark to inaugurate Assembly. With intermediation, necessarily, for the infancy. Not Authorised, only birthed.

FIRST PERIOD OF DELIBERATIVE ASSEMBLY: '<u>INAUGURATION (BY SPECULATION)</u>'

(THE MOST ACCELERATED PERIOD OF ASSEMBLY!)

'SPECULATION' – TO RESOLVE THE <u>DILEMMA OF INAUGURATION</u>:

THERE CAN BE NO DELIBERATORS WITHOUT ASSEMBLY. BUT: THERE CAN BE NO ASSEMBLY WITHOUT DELIBERATORS.

RESOLUTION:

THE BENIGN SUMMONED WORLDLY RESOURCES! TO COMMENCE SPECULATIVE ASSEMBLY! 'SPECULATION': THE MEANS OF INTERMEDIATION BETWEEN DELEGATED ASSEMBLYMEN AND INAUGURAL DELIBERATORS.

METHOD:

i.   ASSEMBLY BY ASSEMBLYMEN.

ii. SELECTIVE INAUGURATION BY DELIBERATORS (IN RESPONSE TO ASSEMBLY BY ASSEMBLYMEN).

iii. SPECULATIVE ASSEMBLY BY ASSEMBLYMEN (IN RESPONSE TO SELECTIVE INAUGURATION BY DELIBERATORS).

iv. (ii AND iii REPEAT UNTIL INAUGURAL ASSEMBLY IS COMPLETE.)

Lawford Road. c.1968

13TH SEPTEMBER 2005

Today is the day that I learned the agonising pain of setting one's hand down onto the upended edges of shattered ceramics. (With a full body weight behind it.) I was manoeuvring around the low roof of an outbuilding, and the pieces were atop a low wall adjacent to it, set into some rigid substrate. The client saw none of it, thankfully.

I can appreciate a preference for the wall to bear some ORNAMENT. I can doubly appreciate the (presumably) strict use of material from within the Area. But I am surprised this made it into the Constitution. My hand is now heavily bandaged, and I expect it will be for some time.

The client showed no embarrassment so I don't expect he ~~had a hand in~~ was involved in this work. In fact, he remarked as if it has long been an inconvenience, though I could see no scarring to his own palms.

The bandaging will slow applications, if only because I will have to protect it from all moisture. This evening, I have used the material from one boiler suit to fashion and fix a mitten onto the end of the left arm of several others, should clients see my injuries and lose confidence in the Solution.

17TH SEPTEMBER 2005

These past few days, bearing an injury as I am, transporting the equipment around the Area – before, between and after applications – has been taking a great deal longer.

    I am not sorry for the discomfort. Perhaps for the first time, the ~~time~~ delay has allowed me to consciously experience – to CONSCIOUSLY experience – my changing stature in relation to the Area. I notice very many things now, and that is indicative of a growing ~~understanding~~ Comprehension.

    The Area is dense with detail added after the inaugural Assembly. Or rather: it is dense with Assembly that has ~~rearranged~~ disarranged that earlier work.

'DISARRANGEMENT' – so called
because it is uniformly HOSTILE to system or
REGULARITY: outbuildings of stacked Stock;
timbers affixed wherever there is any purchase
(at all); scars, fissures and incisions where there
was previously who-knows-what joined.

There is FRENZY to the disarrangement –
a pragmatism not simply of means, but also of*
[*undisclosed] ends.

De Beauvoir Town. c.1968

Do NOT go into clients' homes, as a rule. To avoid causing damage* [*Constitutional infringement]. (Also: if the Solution spilled onto soft furnishings it would be immediately, uncomfortably, and starkly clear just how corrosive it is.)

But today, a TERRACED client (mercifully rare) – leaving no choice but to pass through their Assembly, at least twice, to administer the Solution to the rear of the building. (Mounting the roof is not practicable. If I could stand to Comprehend the Area that way then none of this would be necessary.)

The Area's insides are PINCHED at waist height, all around. Those pinched lengths are only ever brittle plaster or soft timber, so they are doubly vulnerable. Flakes and splinters give way as I fail to make graceful passage through these Constitutional wormholes.

They have several outbuildings around their grounds, including one uncommonly decrepit. ("We refused to have it improved.") Inside, another Stock Assembly, identically HOMESPUN, waist high and the same in width and depth. An enormous copper bowl resting in the hollow atop. Clear PRIDE in this relic – either that, or CRUEL RELISH from the arrangement of their Stock, as if to maximise the combined area of its surfaces and so also, the WORKLOAD it promises to me. Whatever. This is all unfamiliar Assembly, so the relish will be entirely mine when the Solution takes effect and my Comprehension outstrips their petty pride.

It all felt of more VIGOUR than ever, and it is beginning to take effect already this evening. Observe. The deep PATINA of the copper signals its history as a water vessel. The thick SOOT around its cradling Assembly confirms: it is all a retrograde means of WATER HEATING.

But the CRUDITY of it! It is not the work of the Assemblymen. The resources convened for this outbuilding and its contents are too feeble.

For all the necessity of the Assemblymen's work, it is an indictment of the COARSENESS of Speculation.

We are all bound by the Constitution, in at least two senses. We are bound TOGETHER by it, but we also freely accept its BONDAGE, because we know it is benevolent (Benign?). So it is naturally discomforting to learn we are bound more discomfortingly than we had thought.

The Speculation between Assemblymen and the earliest Deliberators was far from perfect, because Speculation is a blunt instrument. It could neither perceive nor foresee the life of the Area with any precision or exactitude. At a point, when inaugural Assembly had concluded, Assembly could only properly continue in the hands of the Deliberators, but they would have to WRESTLE it away from the Assemblymen. An insurrection was needed. No – a THOUSAND INSURRECTIONS were needed. A thousand insurrections, all too ~~capillarious~~ capillarous for the Assemblymen to silence, or even identify.

A few of the Stock disarranged, here. An embellishment to a piece of Assembly, there. No time to wait for a more sophisticated means – start now, today, alone.

Only Deliberators pass THAT wall every day; only Deliberators will notice a sprinkling of ornament added to it overnight; only Deliberators will respond in kind, in a manner similarly insurgent but differently realised. LIKE Speculation, this disarrangement is Deliberation through the medium of Assembly (for that is all they knew!). UNLIKE Speculation, it is to the exclusion of all those we may thank sincerely for their imperfect Assemblies, but now insistently demand move on.

De Beauvoir Town. c.1973

SECOND PERIOD OF DELIBERATIVE ASSEMBLY:
'<u>EXCLUSION (BY DISARRANGEMENT)</u>'.

(THE MOST BRAZEN PERIOD OF ASSEMBLY!)

'<u>DISARRANGEMENT</u>' – TO RESOLVE THE <u>DILEMMA OF EXCLUSION</u>:

ONLY ASSEMBLYMEN ARE EXPERIENCED IN ASSEMBLY. BUT: WITH INAUGURAL ASSEMBLY <u>COMPLETE</u>, AND THE METHOD OF SPECULATION <u>OBSOLETE</u>, ASSEMBLY MUST BE DECISIVELY AND FORCIBLY PASSED TO DELIBERATORS.

RESOLUTION:

'<u>DISARRANGEMENT</u>' – THE MEANS
OF <u>EXCLUSION</u> OF ASSEMBLYMEN,
FOR DELIBERATORS; THE MEANS
TO <u>APPRENTICE</u> TO ASSEMBLY, FOR
DELIBERATORS!

METHOD:

i. <u>ONE DELIBERATOR</u> BEGINS TO
<u>DISARRANGE</u> THE INAUGURAL ASSEMBLY,
TO SIGNAL THE <u>OBSOLESCENCE</u> OF
DELEGATED ASSEMBLY.

ii. <u>ANOTHER DELIBERATOR</u> SEES THAT INAUGURAL ASSEMBLY HAS BEEN DISARRANGED AND <u>DOES SIMILARLY</u>, TO SIGNAL CONCURRENCE.

iii. (i AND ii <u>REPEAT</u> UNTIL DELIBERATIVE ASSEMBLY IS <u>EXCLUSIVELY</u> AMONG DELIBERATORS.)

Lawford Road. c.1968
Balls Pond Road. c.1970

3RD OCTOBER 2005

This afternoon, with a client:

A fish pond, just where I need to set up. I look at her aghast. Her reaction is as if I am in awe of the koi carp.

There is little one can say in the face of that.

The water is clear and the pond lining still visible beneath it, as dark and frictionless as the day it was installed – which I would date to no more than six months ago.

Experiences like this one remain rare, but are indicative of a certain (sure) creep towards Constitutional complacency of a very particular kind – brazen; almost proud of its transparency* [*lit.]. Did she think I wouldn't notice the Extraction? No. Does she care? Doubly: no – it is an assertive affront, not apologetic. Her back garden is overlooked by three other homes directly, and perhaps ten others indirectly.

The IRONY: I now Comprehend there was a time when disarrangement, broadcast discretely in ways like this, was the lifeblood of the Area. But that time has long passed.

When I embarked with the Solution I had in mind a typical home within the Area. An oblong, give or take. Perhaps with a lean-to.

That mental image seems very distant now, both in outline and detail.

This morning, in place of an outbuilding to mirror their neighbours', like all the others in this short terrace: a low, circular Assembly of Stock arranged radially (only three or four courses) around the base of a steel barrel (or more likely two, or even three, joined end-to-end and stacked). BLACKENING over almost all of the visible surfaces, inside and out. The beginnings of buddleia amid the jasmine engulfing it, sewn through the innumerable rust holes. The client insisted his home once knew a life as a MANUFACTORY, ~~melting~~ smelting zinc (?). Whatever – today it acquired another new life, as an almighty obstacle for me.

The spaces between the circular* [*stacked!] Stock were near impossible to penetrate. And protected, for the most part, by a still-viscous tarring that SUFFOCATES any material or instrument coming into contact with it. For the time being, I shall have to reconcile with not fully Comprehending this monolith.

To attempt to date it: the very end of the period of disarrangement, for certain. It is a SIGNAL OF EXCLUSION of the Assemblymen at the extreme of imagination. Thick black clouds must have risen from this point for many years, visible throughout the Area. Any remaining

Assemblymen that had still failed to read the signs would have choked on the realisation (lit.) that they were no longer welcome. A funnel of dense black is irrefutable, but even more so is the Deliberative intensity of a manufactory – those clouds did not only signal defiance to the Assemblymen, but also their obsolescence: Assembly of any ~~scale~~ ambition CAN AND WILL now be achieved by the Deliberators, together, alone, as one. Almost a gesture to humiliate: when Deliberators can conjure such dynamic, compound substances, digging and baking the ground level* [*that is, the original manufacture of Stock] seems pathetic, crude, in comparison.

directions. The Solution must already be at work on Stock with a similar history, because I can Comprehend many other examples besides this one: glass panes, printed matter, footwear, furniture (others still indistinct). The Area once kept its own dairy cattle for sustenance, I am quite sure.

For those Constituents who have been of the Area for long enough, it is a place of hay, heifers and smithies as much as eucalyptus, magnolia and bulletins.

De Beauvoir home, before General Improvement Area works. c.1973

9TH OCTOBER 2005

Some relief, after the trials of yesterday.

For one, a newly fabricated mitten. With my
workload, the wound reopens almost daily.
The inside of the first mitten had long been
encrusted, but more recently it had been starting
to seep through and show on the outside. Now:
confidence restored, on both sides.

    Moreover: today, some first rate run-off
(drainage). Waste ~~water~~ Solution directed exactly
as one would expect it from the Constitution.
Yesterday was an anomaly; most of the Area
is at least this proficient. More immediately
gratifying: a regular set of Stock surfaces to
work with!

So often, there have been too many OBSTRUCTIONS to even keep to a schedule, far beside the inconsistencies of the early Assembly. Every one confounds the application process, in penetration, volume and vigour: ~~areas~~ patches of Stock inconsistent with the rest; a length of timber fixed arbitrarily – or holes where there once was. NONE of these things I anticipated in advance. But they are all MOMENTS OF ASSEMBLY and they all need to be Comprehended, in spite of the inconvenience each and every one presents.

I told today's client of yesterday's zinc smelter claim – "probably true," he said, VERBATIM: "the industry grew up like a fungus around people's homes". LIKE A FUNGUS! Tumorous disarrangement – Deliberative Assembly at risk of ingesting itself.

De Beauvoir home, after General Improvement Area works. c.1973

11TH OCTOBER 2005

SYLLOGISM:

i. Disarrangement tends to incoherence.

ii. The Area is the result of two centuries of finely attuned Deliberative Assembly. Neither it, nor any part of it, is incoherent.

iii. CONCLUSION: There was a moment in the Deliberative Assembly of the Area when the incoherence of disarrangement was reversed.

De Beauvoir Town. 1972

14TH OCTOBER 2005

The OFFENCE OF MISGIVINGS. Not since the very first applications has a client sought to test the integrity of the* [*integrity testing!] Solution.

I ENTERTAIN these buildings. I circuit them – I vault them, I skim them, I skate them. I DANCE AROUND THEM. I blandish the Constitution, entirely for its own sake – for the sake of its Reconstitution. But first, I must please ~~Constituents~~ clients. I cannot apply the Solution without their consent, so that is my most immediate priority.

This woman could well see how much she had offended me. She spent much of the afternoon doing little more than reneging. At first, she piqued my interest. She told me, many years ago, she lived in a SHRINKING HOME. But she did not mean by this what one would assume. The process entailed no dis-Assembly. The STRUCTURE of her home remained unchanged. Rather, the HABITABLE PORTION of it changed. Something akin to A VESSEL SINKING INTO SEAS ON ALL SIDES, until only a few rooms were not submerged – or, as she put it, without "the climate of a peat bog".

As tenuous as the ring of her reasoning still is this evening, this is why she had misgivings about the Solution. (She claimed.) By how much would the Wash penetrate? Does it operate consistently across surfaces? Will it attack ("ATTACK"!) portions already vulnerable disproportionately?

Of course, I know the answer to none of these questions. But it is outrageous that she

should think they should supervene the more
foundational (lit.) purpose of Reconstitution.

De Beauvoir home before General Improvement works. c.1972

15TH OCTOBER 2005

Continuing recollections of yesterday.

Amidst all my discontent, I MISSED the fulcrum moment that my Comprehension has grown to ENCOMPASS, but not yet NAMED. (Names will not be needed in the Reconstitution, but they help for the time being.)

   The woman's sinking home is not the one I applied to yesterday. This home, she came to live in by trust, "by the trust of the Association".

S/S page 3   Photo 4a x4b
De Beaver 7

THE ASSOCIATION: this is what brought the period of disarrangement to a close. Having worked – separately but together – to disarrange the Area and claim it as their own from the Assemblymen, the Deliberators found an equally stark, and equally urgent, demand for reorientation: away from the PRECIPICE OF INCOHERENCE and towards IMPROVEMENT and COMPLETION. And this could only be achieved in unison, in common, in TRUST. The labour of disarrangement would be coordinated – for the first time, Deliberation would be facilitated verbally, and not through brute Assembly.

(I also now remember her mention of keeping rabbits for slaughter in that old home. Some things are best forgotten.)

Culford Road. 1972
De Beauvoir Trust Share Certificate. 1974

**THIRD PERIOD OF DELIBERATIVE ASSEMBLY:
'MATURATION (BY ASSOCIATION)'**

**(THE MOST SOPHISTICATED PERIOD OF
ASSEMBLY!)**

**'ASSOCIATION' – TO RESOLVE THE DILEMMA
OF MATURITY:
THE INCOHERENCE OF DISARRANGEMENT
MUST BE REFINED TO BE THE EQUAL OF
THE SYMMETRY, BUT WITHOUT REVERSING
ITS ACHIEVEMENT OF ASSEMBLY
EXCLUSIVELY BETWEEN DELIBERATORS.**

RESOLUTION:

**ASSOCIATION: THE MEANS OF REVERSING
THE INCOHERENCE OF DISARRANGEMENT;
THE MEANS OF EMBOLDENING
DELIBERATORS!**

METHOD:

i. **A SMALL NUMBER OF DELIBERATORS
    CEASE ASSEMBLY BY DISARRANGEMENT
    IN FAVOUR OF ASSEMBLY BY COMMON
    ASSOCIATION.**
ii. **DELIBERATORS OF COMMON
    ASSOCIATION REJECT ALL ASSEMBLY BY
    DISARRANGEMENT.**

iii. **MORE DELIBERATORS CEASE <u>ASSEMBLY BY DISARRANGEMENT</u> IN FAVOUR OF <u>ASSEMBLY BY COMMON ASSOCIATION</u>.**

iv. **(ii AND iii REPEAT UNTIL <u>REFINED ASSEMBLY</u> IS COMPLETE).**

De Beaver newsletter 16. 1974
Buckingham Road. c.1975

23RD OCTOBER 2005

It began to rain part-way through an application today (for the first time). I persevered until soaked through but the client protested and, truth be told, I was concerned the Solution could have less effect in this weather.

We sheltered in his garage as it passed. He implored me to remove my boiler suit, now a few tones of grey darker. I should have trusted my ~~instincts~~ method and declined. In the event, he visibly recoiled upon seeing my normal dress underneath, and the bandages under my mitten.

I tried to fashion a seat among the boxes but he forbade it, lest the rainwater still running off me damaged their contents. He removed the lid from one, revealing what must have been hundreds of photographic prints and negatives. This is all he needed to show to make his point, but my Comprehension of late is so KEEN that I recognised them to all be, unmistakably, of the Area.

Some of the images are recognisable from the bulletins. Countless others were entirely unfamiliar, but doubtless depict the Area.*
[*Recognisable locations.]

Tempted, I succumbed and pocketed as many as I could when his back was turned.

The NOVELTY OF RESEMBLANCE passed even before I packed away for the day. Now I am left with dozens of images to throw on the pile of COMMENTARY along with the bulletins that I know so many of them from. The specious

supposition that they somehow CONTAIN
Deliberation was seductive in the moment. But I
cannot now return them! I will just have to keep
them locked away, indefinitely. Some may be of
use, later (as notation, or secondary reference).
It's possible.

Image for De Beaver newsletter 6. 1972

47/123/4

7

Image for De Beaver newsletter. 1972

De Beauvoir Town. c.1972

"RED TAPE" FENCE . . .
Cutting through "red tape,"
committee members of the De
Beauvoir Association, Hackney, erected a seven-foot fence
around a derelict site, opposite
Kingsland Catholic School—to
cut down its potential danger.

27TH OCTOBER 2005

A certain vertigo, approaching the third storey.
It's never happened before. The client stood the
whole time in his front garden, looking up at me.
Squinting, I remember – poor eyes, or, realising
my terror. My face to the Stock, my back to the
~~thoroughfare~~ Northern Perimeter. Him, too – if
only he could see it. All the years he's lived here,
it's invisible to him now.

Some time for respite afterwards (he insists).
Some time for reminiscences of Association. With
commentary he fetches, as I regain composure.

These distractions, so often unbearable. But
this ~~barricade~~ ~~hoarding~~ SCREEN. A privilege
to know, even only in commentary! A tentative
step to amending disarrangement? 'Reverse-
disarrangement'? No – it bears a CONTINUITY
OF MEANS from before: a Deliberator takes a
piece from one Assembly and recombines it with
another, many times over. Aggregation – simple
aggregation.

But now? Now, PROPINQUITY. Many
Deliberators, working in concert. As a MUSCLE:
working when its fibres are contracted together,
and not sprawling, like some over-forked straw.
A more MUSCULAR DELIBERATION!

A new strategy: Assembly, established through
Deliberation, established through Assembly, in
turn. (As future Deliberators watch on.)

Hackney Gazette 28th February. 1969

30TH OCTOBER 2005

In the photographs, this man recurs.

Among Deliberators – but not a Deliberator
himself. (Reminding of me, in the Solution
suit. A practiced pose. All buttoned up. Give
nothing away!)

I knew I knew him; the bulletins.

(A practiced pose.) Why study him?

De Beauvoir Road. 1972
De Beauvoir Road. 1972
Image cropped for De Beaver newsletter 9. 1972
De Beauvoir Road. 1972

31ST OCTOBER 2005

The man who showed me the Screen was a keen
Deliberator. I couldn't see it before, among the
lines, but come this morning: yes. He was there
when the Screen was Assembled, when common
Association was found. He should be able to
identify the man in the photographs. He could.

The man in the photographs is an AUTHORISER.

Like all Authorisers, he had NO STAKE in the
Area.* His only interest, the only reason he came
to the Area, was to RENEW himself. Without
Authorisation, these people are like particulates
– properly viewed, at a distance: cloud of smoke,
gone, out of the imagination. An attribute shorn
of its attribute, is nothing.

[*They are not like the Benign – they rely upon changing, not unchanging. I challenge anyone to Authorise unchange!]

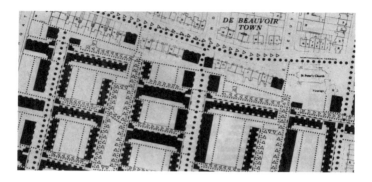

Like any Authoriser, this man is known in the recipience of his attribute. That is how they MUST be known – because it is all they have to extend into the world, and because continuous recipience is their means of renewal, of LONGEVITY. Always, looking for a tiredness, a FATIGUE, to accept as an invitation to Authorise, and to renew.

In its state of Disarrangement, this man circled the Area, and came to view it as his latest NEW means of renewal. Indifferent, it could have been any object for him, in all respects but one: this, the Area, was, at this moment, the one his eye was trained upon.

The INCOHERENCE OF DISARRANGEMENT was a tiredness he would accept as an invitation. That, and the always perceptible tremor of mourning, the lament for the loss of the Symmetry. A NEW SYMMETRY was Authorised! Demanding Extraction – TOTAL EXTRACTION. TOTALLY OFFENSIVE to all Deliberators; a TOTAL OFFENSIVE against all Deliberative Assembly.

De Beauvoir Town Study. 1969

2ND NOVEMBER 2005

That man, the Deliberator, and his commentary. He APPROACHED me today, on Englefield. As I was practicing my stride.

I didn't know it was him. He looks very different this way – anonymous. His scalp tips forwards, released by years-extended vertebrae.

As he neared, and those vertebrae contracted, and that scalp reclined, I – concede – I panicked.

I did not want to deceive him! He does not know me this way. When I have forgotten that in the past, it has brought me close to disaster. I could see he was gesturing to me, but I was already making an about-turn. He called after me but I kept walking, faster.

I did not want to deceive him!

To home, into the suit, and out again, to find him. Eventually – heading up to Ardleigh. His look to me had three moments, I remember: stupefaction; vexation; favour. Good Constituents, both of us, by the end of it.

This evening, it has got me to thinking.

The studies of that man – that AUTHORISER.

The Deliberators knew he was coming. They knew the Authorial mastery he represented, and they knew they would have to make representations to him – AGAINST him. They knew they would have to display to him their own mastery, to vouch for their own Assembly, against the one he would bring.

But when the time came to make representations to him, they represented only himself – back to himself. They called his bluff!

What else but your GUISE warrants your Authorisations?

The look of yours: it's not one of intimidation, at all – it's one of ~~recognition~~ SELF-RECOGNITION.

De Beauvoir Road. 1972

I have more to hand than I realised.

I have had these photographs, from this time when there came a new guise, a FOIL.

It carries over from commentary the likeness of DISTANCE, and I am not sure even my stature can yet see over its horizon. (I have tried soaking some of this material in the Solution but it has little effect. It only attacks – crumbles to pulp.)

There is some, limited, range available – more than there would be, if it were not for the Solution.

A visit from an Authoriser is never welcome, but this one held at least some good fortune. The Deliberation of Association, of the Screen, of the

CONSPICUOUSLY TOGETHER, was newly
emerged and the lesson (extraction!) to be
had from their artful visitor was all it needed
to become airborne – to take flight from the
Assembly, almost. Making representations
– soon, of all kinds of enunciations, from
throughout the AUTHORIAL CANON.

The Authoriser – out-manoeuvred! He HAD to
recognise this PHANTASM as one of his own,
lest he lose his own means of sustenance, his own
ONLY means of existence! He could not CALL
OUT this Authorial phantasm because he would
have to be able to RECOGNISE it first.

(Whose works are those in front of you?
Is that man dressed as you, or you as him?)

The Deliberators had manoeuvred to leave
the Authoriser with a choice: CALL OUT in
uncertainty and risk groundlessness if you are
wrong* [*the CLOUD OF SMOKE, without

attribute], or continue as normal, knowing your words and works may not be your own, and your Authorisations, for the Deliberators, only tacit admissions of IMPOTENCE.

In this DILEMMA, an Authoriser will always choose the latter. But now, today, there are no longer any Deliberators, only

CONSTITUENTS. That is why Authorisers have regained confidence NOW, and it is why I cannot sidestep this indistinction. I cannot risk carrying the SPORES OF AUTHORISERS into the Reconstitution, for them to GERMINATE again there, as they are managing to, NOW, TODAY, in the Constitution. My project, my ENTIRE project, to this point, has been to EXTRICATE the truly DELIBERATIVE Assembly from the Authorial, and that is what I must continue to do.

Probably St Peters Crypt. 1972

10TH NOVEMBER 2005

After the great **STRIDES** of recent weeks – in the final few steps, an impasse.* [*A fog? Seen on approach; no better for it on arrival.] The problem, after this **THRESHOLD**, is an almost **TOTAL INDISTINCTION** from within the Area, and without.

    With this shadow play, this **PEERING**, the visiting Authoriser was bound. But others – Authorisers, who had never thought to target the Area – were soon similarly **SNARED**.

Annual Report 69- 70

The Association is now beginning to see the return on all the hard work which has been put in over our 2½ years of life. Our picture shows De Beauvoir children enjoying a puppet show at a celebratory party to mark the opening of the local-based De Beauvoir Trust's first modernised homes by Mr. Paul Channon, a junior housing minister. We also had a party for adult members in the evening at the Benyon. But we have much more to celebrate. The Council has declared the so-called "central area" as a General Improvement Area; and local people are now

And thereafter, the Authorial efforts of each are indistinct: it is impossible to know which is the copy, and which is the original. It was all necessary to penetrate the channels that would bring the resources of Authorisers cascading into the Area.

After the showhouse opening, a puppet show, followed by an ice-cream-and-jelly feast gave over 100 children of De Beauvoir Town something to remember ...

.... and their parents will be talking for a long time about the "knees up" in the Benyon Arms. The De Beauvoir community – of all ages – really got involved!

*On October 26, it was announced that, in Central Government reorganisation, Peter Walker (formerly Minister of Housing and Local Government) would be in charge of a new department – Department of the Environment. Among those responsible to Mr. Walker is Julian Amery (Minister for Housing and Construction) who will be assisted by Paul Channon (Parliamentary Under-Secretary of State).

Ideal-Standard Limited,
Ideal Works, Hull, HU5 4JE, Yorkshire,
England.
Telephone 0482 46461 Telex 52113

I D E A L
STANDARD

At least – I can say (I can ONLY say), I IMAGINE it was necessary! The Solution made legible to me only those Deliberative works which are indivisible from the Assembly. These, from this time, of Improvement, are not. These are airborne; aloof.

Gazette

Circulating throughout:
HACKNEY, CLAPTON, STOKE NEWINGTON,
STAMFORD HILL, SHOREDITCH, STEPNEY,
HOXTON, BETHNAL GREEN, ISLINGTON,
TOTTENHAM, WALTHAMSTOW, LEYTON.

PUBLISHED TUESDAY AND FRIDAY

No 20

New plan for De Beauvoir goes on show

DE BEAUVOIR residents are being asked for their final verdict on the experimental road closure schemes, which has been in operation since last April. An exhibition starting to-day (Tuesday) seeks reactions to the De Beauvoir General Improvement Area Blueprint, which has been formulated by Hackney Council planners and the residents' Environmental Committee.

A special issue of the community newspaper, "The Beaver" (financed for the occasion by Hackney Council) calls on residents to take a long, cool look at the plan as a whole, and not to "dismiss the whole package just because the road closures may have soured your vision."

The exhibition is in the crypt of St. Peter's, North-church Terrace, and is open from 5 p.m. till 9 p.m. today and Thursday, and from 3 p.m. till 9 p.m. on Wednes-

corner where the two roads meet."

The association also want the nearby Whitmore Bridge closed to traffic because of the danger to residents if it is widened.

Highly critical of the timing of the exhibition is secretary of the De Beauvoir New Town Association, Mrs. Emelie Chalk. She is writing to the Department of the Environment to complain that mothers with young children will find it difficult to get to St. Peter's to put

DURING
experim
acciden
fell by
a saving
estimate
which is
when fi
to April

In Down
10 in tl
before,
And on
from fi

De Beauvoir Association Annual Report. 1969–70
Ideal Standard Modernisation Bulletin: De Beauvoir houses. 1970

ROADS: CRUCIA[L]
ON WEDNESDAY

[A]PRIL 1975

[...]onths of the
[...]es the
[...]ads affected
[...]his represents
[...]ty of an
[...]day's prices,
[...] to £40,000
[...]l year (up

[...]s fell from
[...]e months
[...] the closures.
[...] the drop was
[...]orthchurch

resolutions backing the road closure.

Few councillors outside the area will be aware of these crucial resolutions. They will certainly have heard of the 800 strong petition last September opposing the closures, but may not know that many of the signatories were led to believe they were petitioning for something quite different – the additional closure of De Beauvoir and Downham roads, which the council has always refused to consider.

The closure of these two roads was
[...]

Public debate at the Crypt

Other schemes nearby show the value placed on road closures – Islington's Marquess Road estate and their plans for the Scott estate, and Hackney's Albion Square. The accident figures speak for themselves. The re-routed commuters may think twice about driving to work.

The cost of a No

If the roads are reopened, a heavy crop of accidents – especially in St. Peter's Way (beside Lockner Rd flats),

Hackney Gazette. 1975
De Beaver newsletter 20. 1975

FOURTH PERIOD OF DELIBERATIVE ASSEMBLY:

'COMPLETION (BY AUTHORISATION)'

(THE FINAL PERIOD OF DELIBERATIVE ASSEMBLY!)

'AUTHORISATION' = TO RESOLVE THE <u>DILEMMA OF COMPLETION</u>:
THE AREA MUST BE <u>COMPLETED</u>, AND THE <u>CONSTITUTION</u> SEALED – WITH ASSURANCE AGAINST FUTURE <u>ADDITION</u> OR <u>EXTRACTION</u>. FROM INSIDE THE AREA, THIS IS ASSURED. FROM OUTSIDE THE AREA, IT IS NOT. THE CONSTITUTION MUST BE ASSURED (SEALED) FROM OUTSIDE THE AREA. BUT FOR THE CONSTITUTION TO STAND, IT MUST BE ENTIRELY THE WORK OF THE <u>AREA</u>!

RESOLUTION:

THE AREA IS DECLARED <u>COMPLETE</u> IN A WORK <u>OF THE AREA</u>, BUT <u>OUTSIDE</u> <u>OF THE AREA</u>.

METHOD:

i.   DELIBERATORS IN COMMON ASSOC-IATION BEGIN TO STRATEGICALLY ~~IMITATE MIMIC~~ <u>PEER</u> AUTHORISERS.
ii. AUTHORISERS BECOME UNABLE TO DISTINGUISH THEIR OWN WORKS FROM THOSE OF DELIBERATORS.
iii. (i AND ii <u>REPEAT</u> UNTIL AUTHORISERS DECLARE THE AREA COMPLETE FROM <u>OUTSIDE OF THE AREA</u>, IN A WORK <u>OF THE AREA</u>).

Ufton Road. 1981

17TH NOVEMBER 2005

The Solution continues, but not in the same way. Its very success – its RECONSTITUTIVE success – has exacted a ringing solitude.

When I am working, I will shift attention towards more recent years, the years of IMPROVEMENT. What will then follow is akin to a conversation of a very particular kind – of alienating the most gracefully talented interlocutor, with talk too obscure, academic, or trivial. Conversation sputters and dims – you are still face-to-face, together, but more alone.* [*all of one!]

This is how it is now, with bookings. One moment, I will be with the Assembly, Comprehending new details of Speculation and Disarrangement, and moving through the years. But when I come to Improvement, we come to a HALT. The life has gone out of it.

But the client! The CLIENT will have many stories – all, fine detail: installed greens, Authorised Screens, Assembly Machines. But they are only stories – COMMENTARY. The Deliberation itself is nowhere to be seen; worst of all, I don't know where to look for it. In these years, it RAN OFF THE STOCK like so much Solution, and reconvened elsewhere. Yes, in commentary – but as well, in the spaces between.

De Beauvoir Square. c.1974
De Beaver newsletter 19. 1975

Today: a lonely conversation with a client was finally annulled with talk of "Colditz barriers". Whatever this refers to, it is not of the Stock, and surely not even of the Area. I let it pass, lest the distance between us grow even greater and our solitude, with it.

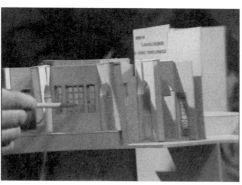

'COLDITZ'

Castle?

1940 – 45: Prisoner of war camp.

1972 – 74: Dramatisation.

PREMISE: Military officers incarcerated within a confining assembly. Conspire to escape.

NOVELTY: Ingenuity of incarcerated; leveraging access through successive spaces, to surrounding space, and beyond.

('TEAM GAME'? Bounded area of play: castle. A competition! For AUTHORIAL CONTROL, of what the castle is – a place of incarceration, or a place of emancipation.)

Colditz. 1972

8TH DECEMBER 2005

No ~~improvement~~ progress – the years of
IMPROVEMENT are so much more in-
Comprehensible than any others. So much from
this time is only Authorial. And so, when it
encounters ME (the antithesis of an Authoriser!)
it REPELS attention.

De Beauvoir General Improvement Area Environmental
Sub-Committee meeting Agenda. 1974

De Beauvoir General Improvement Area

There will be a meeting of the ENVIRONMENTAL SUB-COMMITTEE on 7th November,
Wednesday, at 8.00pm in the Marriage Room at Hackney Town Hall, Mare Street.

A G E N D A

Reading of previous minutes

1.00 Temporary road closures.

2.00 Permanent road closures.

3.00 Working drawings for some of the road closures to be presented by the
      Council for information and Residents' Committee remarks.

4.00 De Beauvoir Square, fire access requires revision to plan.

5.00 Englefield Road rear access.

6.00 Industrial nuisance.

7.00 Renaming of sections of road created by permanent closures.

8.00 Temporary community facilities at 12 Ufton Road.

Set date of next meeting.

My scale against the Area is so much greater than it once was, and my SCOPE so much broader, that, when confronted with Deliberation like this, with pained pretensions to the MICROSCOPIC, I am left hunched and contorted – all squinting eyes and senseless fingers.

The Authoriser came in 1972 and it is from this time that Deliberation becomes so much more difficult to locate. From thereon, it FRACTURES: it splits dramatically, with each piece retaining strength of substance from the whole.

(No – suggests a permanent weakening.)

Better – it COPPICES: its energies are divided through care and foresight.

(No – suggests only senseless growth kept in check.)

Better – it REFRACTS: its parts are divided but in steady relation.

(No – suggests blindness; not able to conceive of direction, much less pursue it.)

De Beauvoir GIA - Programme

FEB

<u>Residents Report</u>

Agenda Conference

MAR

Housing Dev't C'tee → i) deferred add
refer   2 months

APR

Planning + Highways C'tee
refer
Finance C'tee
COUNCIL APPROVAL

MAY

RAHY   Sect 6   Advise DOE   Road names
(DBSq)   (lamp closures)

Publication (212)

JUNE

DOE DECISION

Inquiry necess   APPROVAL

JULY

Apply to GLC   Apply to GLC   Prepare tenders
(lamp closures)   (road names)

up to 9/12 delay

AUG

                                GLC APPROVAL   Invite tenders

SEPT

                                                      Any modifications,
                                                      amendments etc

OCT

        8th (existing temp closure order expires)

                                                      Housing Dev't C'tee
                                                      APPROVAL or Defer

NOV

Commence works
De B. Square

DEC

                                Start Works
                                Jan '76

Preparation of working drawings
Specifications, quantities etc

Whatever. If the force at the centre of it all – the fracturing club, the coppicing blade, the refracting prism – will remain hidden, then I will have to know it from others, who lived through the event. (One certainty about Association: it incorporates many!)

I will have no choice but to pay attention to my clients.

General Improvement Area public exhibition, Rose Lipman Building. 1977
De Beauvoir General Improvement Area draft programme. 1975
Northchurch Road. 1977

Clients, today: their garden, a credit to them.
Clearly already timeless by the time Assembly
ceased. Consequently, now celebrated as much
by the VENOMOUS as by the rest of us. I was
only too happy to spend the time working at
height. The sun was scraping the back of my
neck by the end, but that I prefer to perforated
ankles.

He – sat there throughout under the
chequered shade of the trelliswork, reclined so
as to fix a stare upon me. (Not any help, but not
any harm, either.)

He is of the Area since 1972. As much as my
leathering neck would allow, I strained to keep
conversation about the Improvement years, and
what is at the centre of it all. A FAVOURABLE
response, but little to say about Improvement, or
Authorisers. (His own man – not one for Peering
others.) His talk was all of dust behind eyelids
and debris behind fingernails. He offered all
apologies for offering no more, but sent me away
with a notice, and an instruction to show it to a
very particular Constituent on Ufton Road.

THIS SATURDAY

AND SUNDAY APRIL 7 & 8

also come and talk about your ideas
for the new playground at the crypt
st.peter's church de beauvoir square
wednesday april 11 th between 4:30-9
de beauvoir association

Invitation flyer. 1973

WANT SOMEWHERE TO PLAY

NOW?

COME TO UFTON ROAD
DOWNHAM ROAD JUNCTION
TO CLEAR THE SITES
FOR OUR FIRST EVER
PLAYGROUND IN DE BEAUVOIR

13TH DECEMBER 2005

A plan applied is a plan approved!

The client at the bottom of Ufton Road had much to say about the Centre. And much commentary to pass on. I have needed some time to make sense of it all.

He managed to talk about the Centre for hours, this man, without ever talking **ABOUT THE CENTRE**. All dates, costs and duties. Like speaking of a shovel with only talk of tin and timber.

So – paraphrasing:

The Centre was a nursery: the Area within the Area. Deliberators, flirting with the *longue durée*, for the first time. The Authoriser had come only a few months before and they knew, for the first time, how great were the stakes in PLOTTING A PATH to Improvement, and Completion – great enough to warrant this protection, away from Peering eyes (lit.), always ~~hoarded~~ behind a hoarding. (Recalling: "an EXPRESSION of De Beauvoirishness," he said; a SIGNAL of the whole, before the whole.)

Time at the Centre accelerated beyond the rest of the Area. It was an ACADEMY, for all ages – schooling adults and children alike, from the elementary Association of the Screen, up. (For good habits – form good habits!) A model, in advance – before ~~full~~ scaled-up execution of the IMPROVEMENT AREA. The potholes could be filled, in calm, before they arrive in the Area, in alarm. A SURE COURSE to Completion – we needed this.

But how much was learned by the outset! The Authoriser had come and gone. As soon as his back was turned, one of his most favoured instruments was quietly put to use. This is why the Centre warrants close reading. The period of Improvement is beyond my Comprehension for now. But before Improvement, came a MODEL OF IMPROVEMENT. And I tower over this, without difficulty.

Ufton Road (corner with Downham Road). 1973

25TH DECEMBER 2005

Further study, of the Centre.

Before full-scale Improvement could emerge
into the light: clearing all trace of the bad habits
from before.

This model Area, still LITTERED with
raging disarrangement. Most of it, incipient –
low-level. But rising above the rest – the most
audacious of all the fungal factories.

Some unknown prior purpose. Some
evidence of moves to Association? If so, then
only FAILED moves – glitched, aborted.

Refrigerators, prams, mattresses: "simple aggregation", but only SENSELESSLY.

Whatever. Whether disarrangement, or defective aggregation, this was only a distraction, a problem to be incinerated away in advance of the real project, just like the space outside.

No, the real project, the real purpose, was to use this VANTAGE POINT to PERFECT PEERING. These were control conditions – a sealed box, behind the barricades. That is all well and good for apprenticing, for stockpiling shadow play, but the MEANS OF IMPROVEMENT would not be requisitioned from inside the hoard.

EIGHT YEARS! The Deliberators needed eight years to Peer all they could at the Authoriser. Eight years is a long time! But the benefits were proven totally, eventually, permanently, after another twenty, when they were capped with COMPLETION. On the face of it, these test theatrics were to discover what common Association ~~could~~ would become. But the key exercise was, simply: by how much to dare. By how much to make representations of Authorisers back to them – teetering at the point where words and works – theirs and ours – are not distinguished.

The Ufton Park Community Centre. 1973–81

2ND JANUARY 2006

TEST THEATRICS, of another kind.

At the end of eight years, they proclaim themselves the culmination, the "EXPRESSION OF DE BEAUVOIRISHNESS" ~~my client~~ the Deliberators sought. But it is only an after-effect. A brief stain on the retina, from the brilliant light that preceded!* [*foreshadowed?]

Eight years, and the Centre was a completed work – an Authorial MASTERPIECE, emerging FULLY FORMED from behind the hoarding. What followed warrants little attention. The important work – the WORK – had been completed. This was a time for CELEBRATION, yes, but a celebration of the POSSIBILITY of it. A celebration that the means for this common ~~Association~~ association has been Assembled.

It scarcely needs to be enacted. But: like any WEAPON OF DETERRENT, when the time comes, to not follow it through would be to leave loose a thread that could cause the whole reasoning of it to UNRAVEL.

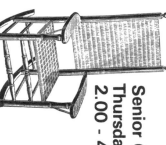

Senior Citizens,
Thursdays
2.00 - 4.00.

Yoga,
Tuesdays
9.45am - 11.45am.

Luncheon Club,
Thursdays
12.30 - 1.30

Coming soon:-

Air Weapon Range,
Legal Advice.

Gingerbread
(One-parent family group).
Mondays 7.30 - 10.00.

Welfare
Rights Advice
Fridays
1.30 - 3.00

The Ufton Centre, 12 Ufton Road, N1.

Tel. 254 2941

The Ufton Centre

Mums & Toddlers,
Mondays 1.30 - 3.30.
Wednesdays
10.30 - 12.30.

Cooking,
Wednesdays

Keep Fit,
Wednesdays 7.30 - 9.30.

Regular Socials.
Meeting Hall for
Weddings and Events.

Tai Chi.

No, the "EXPRESSION OF DE
BEAUVOIRISHNESS" was played out before
any of this – also with the repetition of the music
hall, but taken to metronomic extremes.

It started as a low murmur: a percussive proposition. Some of the detail could be learned from the Authoriser (PEERING over his shoulder!) but the rest had to be Assembled anew, from the ground up, from first principles. If the children were going to begin to have a properly Deliberative training, it would need to be SCORED.

WEEK 6 – PLAYSCHEME

DATE	DETAILS	IN	OUT	BALANCE		
31·08·81	cooking ingredients		·84		M I	F1 ✓
"	trip money	3·75			C O	F2
"	subs	2·79			S	F3
"	trip money	·75			CO	F4
01·09·81	cooking ingredients		·35		M J	F5 ✓
"	Pool cues & tips		7·60		E Q	F6 ✓
"	Trip money	7·00			C O	F7
"	" "	20·75			C O	F8
"	subs	3·60			S	F9
"	Bus fares to St Newington		5·00	✕	F	F10
2·9·81	Soap from canteen	20·00			T R	F11
"	Coach fare to Southend		85·00		C H	F12 ✓
"	Inflatable contribution		10·00	✕	A C/E Q	F13
"	subs	4·05½ / 6·06½			S	F14
"	bus fares to George Sylvester		1·34		F	F15 ✓
3·9·81	Bus fares to Elephant + Castle		5·00	✕	F	F16
"	subs	4·18			S	F17
4·9·81	fares to Spitalfield Farm		3·00	✕	F	F18
"	subs	11·82			S	F19
"	replacement LP record		3·25	✕	A/E	F20
"	further expenses to Spitalfields Farm		2·98		F	F21 ✓
07·09·81	from John Gibson pool table + football table	200·00		−94·19½ 94·20	ADV	F22
"	from John Gibson		276·00		E/A	F23 ✓
10·09·81	film developing	92·00	4·23	−78·19½ −82·42½	ADV M I	F24 F25 ✓

The Centre is a bittersweet realisation. It is a humiliation of the Solution. Comprehension from a more favourable ratio of scale, yes, and from my own, greater stature. But it was only possible within an illustration of the Area! Even the children enjoyed greater stature – that was half of the purpose.

But: it has directed me towards the path plotted by the Deliberators through Improvement, as it had done for them. Already, I can begin to see the same trajectory in later works of rigorous, Authorial monotony – all showing a trail leading out from the Centre.

The Ufton Centre opening party. 1981
The Ufton Centre playscheme rota. 1981
The Ufton Centre playscheme accounts. 1981

Would you tick in the boxes, what facilities you have, and whether they are shared with another family or not, and if they are provided with hot water.

FACILITY	OWN USE	SHARED USE	NONE	HOT WATER	
Kitchen sink	○	○	○	Yes ○ No ○	12.0,1,2,3
Bath or Shower	○	○	○	Yes ○ No ○	13.0,1,2,3
Wash Handbasin	○	○	○	Yes ○ No ○	14.0,1,2,3
Inside lavatory	○	○	○		15.0,1,2,3
Outside lavatory	○	○	○		16.0,1,2,3
Garden	○	○	○		17.0,1,2,3

Do you own a car? YES ○   18.0
                  NO ○   18.1

Do you own a motorcycle?
                  YES ○   18.2
                  NO ○   18.3

If YES , is it kept   IN A GARAGE? ○   18.4
                  IN THE STREET? ○   18.5
                  ELSEWHERE? ○   18.6

Does your home suffer from any of the following faults?

	A LOT	SOME	NONE	
RISING DAMP	○	○	○	19.0,1,2
LEAKING ROOF	○	○	○	20.0,1,2
ROTTING WOODWORK	○	○	○	21.0,1,2
CRUMBLING PLASTER	○	○	○	22.0,1,2
CRACKED/ BULGING BRICKWORK	○	○	○	23.0,1,2
ANY OTHERS	_____			24.0,1,2
	_____			25.0,1,2

What sorts of heating do you use?
           GAS ○   26.0
           ELECTRIC ○   26.1
           OIL ○   26.2
           PARAFFIN ○   26.3
           COAL OR COKE ○   26.4

Is your heating
         GOOD ○   27.0
         ADEQUATE ○   27.1
         INADEQUATE ○   27.2

De Beauvoir Association Southern Area Action Group Residents Survey. 1972

I have been thinking, I need more of the same.

I lose track of things in the Improvement years. At the Centre, forms of Deliberation were incubated that are beyond my Comprehension. To EXPLICATE the path plotted from the Centre, and follow them along it – this is the best chance I have to Reconstitute the Improvement.

What can be gleaned (cleaned?) with the Solution is limited. But the IRONY that it now brings other returns, on occasion, from Constituents, in conversation, both the ones that Improved, and others who benefited from the Centre only indirectly.* [*Returns from conversation so much more hard won than a simple application, executed in silence.]

So I continue – and even Comprehend, from time to time, though always from the time before Improvement. Yesterday – the olfactory drift of printers' CELLULOSE along De Beauvoir Road, and the wintering dust from plaster ornaments, prepared for distribution across the Area, along Ufton Grove. Last week, along Lockner – the putrid stench of CAT FOOD manufacture, and the rattle-racket of MANGLES in production.

But this man, today – the first caller of his kind. He saw one of my notices and called for a Wash. He is NOT OF THE AREA! He comes here to worship. This is how he saw the notice.

He was INSISTENT – insistent that he was right; insistent that his home is within the Area. He isn't – IT isn't. I've seen it! It overlooks the Area, among the Towers to the south. He protests: the Benign and the Area are of common origin; the church is the work of the Benign; this is his church; ergo – he is of the Area.

No.

That would have been that, but for curiosity. This evening, I thought about his words as I considered the Symmetry, and noticed something I'm not sure I have before. I took it down from the wall, turned the frame around, removed the retaining pins, the backing, the illustration – leaving only the window mount board in place.

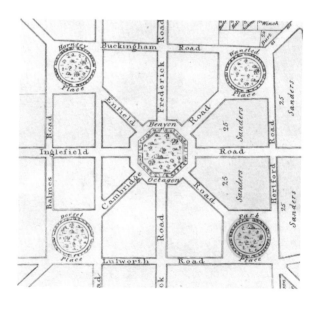

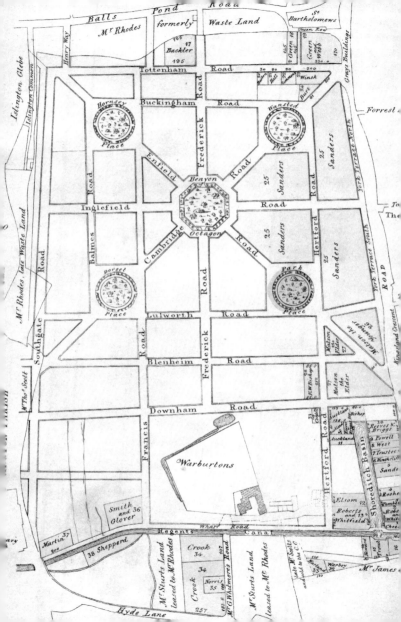

This larger ~~Area~~ area – extending down to this man's home, and beyond.

I called him back – he, surprised to hear from me. And not a little hostile, until I retracted my refusal (through GRITTED TEETH) and suggested a time for his ("very own") Period Charm Wash.

I am not swayed by his unreasonable (UNREASONED) insistences. My discovery today confirms only a continuity. He was never a part of the Symmetry – less even than us, less even than in illustration.

The eye follows De Beauvoir (Frederick?) Road south, only to find it truncated at Downham Road by an irregular wedge (debris from above?) – an *ex ante* termination, not to be restored.

But a continuity, there is. Within the talk he imposed on me, there were moments in the more distant past resembling Speculation, or Disarrangement.

All of this raises a discomforting spectre – if that place knew a time more Deliberative, what's to say his continuity doesn't extend to there? And if that is the case, then what's to say it doesn't have vestiges within the Constitution?

Whatever. I have nothing to lose. And perhaps even, something to gain.

Plan for Beauvoir Town Estate. 1821
Downham Road (south side). c.1968

7TH JANUARY 2006

It's morning and I returned home an hour ago. My hands are raw with cold – it's taken this long to write legibly. I have spent close to a day applying the Solution to a single wall, and close to a day ignoring what I knew the whole time: it won't work here.

After an hour, it became clear that it was having no effect. My client returned indoors but I persevered. And now, that was yesterday.

I have nothing against this man. His company is no more unpleasant than any other's. His home, however – a **CORROSIVE** to my palms, my project, my **PERSON**.

When he could first see that I was struggling, he went inside and returned with illustrations, "should they help". I told him, I have tried that before and the paper only saturates and crumbles.

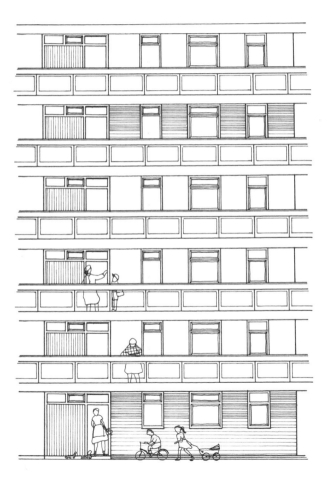

His assembly: it is brick, in part, but even this is not the Stock. (No doubt, it originates somewhere DISTANT; it has none of the glorious POROSITY of the Stock.) The rest, poured concrete – poured, in situ, to distribute itself throughout the mass, seeping into crevices, without any Deliberation, at all.

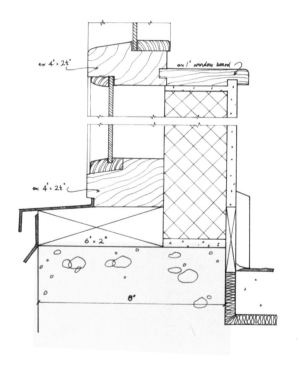

Downham Road. c.1969
De Beauvoir Town development. Part 3. 4-person flats.
Block P6. 1968
De Beauvoir Town development. Block F. Part 2. 1967

De Beauvoir Estate. 1967

The Solution has been a SUCCESS. I must not
forget that. It would be too easy to become
dejected. I ~~devised~~ PERFECTED that method,
entirely originally, for a particular application,
tailored to the demands of the situation.* [*An
existential crisis, nothing less!] How does
one go about surmounting two centuries of
Deliberative Assembly? How does one shift the
ratio of scale, to make all of that singularly
COMPREHENSIBLE?

How many others could even APPROACH
such a question?

The Solution is, in essence (every-sense),
as we all are, OF THE AREA – from the Stock;
from its origination; from the origins of the Area.
All, entirely peculiar to itself.

But – perhaps this invitation, to begin to
know the Towers, could be of some use.

Considering:

The Centre is (IS) Improvement at a diminished
scale, in advance of the event. (Just as any 'good'
Authoriser would pursue, in the first instance!)

The Area has an even, human scale. Not so
to the South. The Towers cast their shadows onto
everything. There is nothing that can put their
summits into shade.

Recalling: the very first client – her talk of
EL HIERRO, 'The Iron'. Rising to a single point,
to a perfect panorama.

By **SURMOUNTING THE TOWERS**, I can surmount the Area and the Towers themselves, at once. From up there, one's field of vision will easily extend to the northern perimeter of the Area, to the western and eastern perimeters, and everywhere between. The Authorisers' work, itself, misused in mimicry of one their own favourite strategies – **PEERED!** All, in turn, a higher strategy worthy of the Centre.

The Ufton Centre. 1981

11TH JANUARY 2006

The cold is pronounced up here. It's a stark cold, the kind that reminds exactly where the exposed islands are on the body. I have found loose patches of roof felt collected in one corner, and I have no shame in recording their utility for keeping warm a foot, or a thigh, or a nape (secured with a spot of bitumen).

It would not be EASY to get up here. With a Solution suit – cut and hemmed around the hips. And a piece of board, salvaged from the Solution equipment, about the size of that of the visiting Authoriser. Practiced holding it as he does; loosely – not over-protective; ~~authoritatively~~ Authorially; knowing the weight of it, but wearing it lightly. ACCESS GRANTED, almost immediately!

STRATEGEM* [*in development]:

I keep away from the edges before dusk, which is when my advantage comes. The sun dips below the horizon (as I see, before any other!). I cover my eyes, for twenty minutes. Thereafter I am dark-adjusted, and a brief window follows when I have a greater chance of seeing than of being seen.

   If I mount the perimeter ledge then my entire field of vision is occupied only by the Area. If one projects a bare foot forwards along the roof felt, incrementally towards the perimeter of the ledge, there is a ridge detectable along that ledge, immediately before the surface turns through ninety degrees in the vertical plane, to begin its sheer descent towards the ground. This ridge is my security – my ridge, my rope!

From this position, it all becomes Comprehensive. The Symmetry is discernible with only slight projection. The Centre, though no longer visible, is almost directly below. Equally so, the Colditz barriers, and the toy vehicles I watch snaking through the Area in homage to them.

Until: at some moment, a window will open out close below me and enter my peripheral vision. It's all that's needed to reintroduce to consciousness the single, unbroken surface that connects me to the objects of my view, far below. From myself to the Tower; from the Tower to the Area – all restored in scale, to parity. Comprehension is shattered and it all becomes in-Comprehensible, once again.

17TH JANUARY 2006

From the ledge: this man, idly scraping his soles
along the street as he walked. Like a living
mockery of the Constitution. I saw him this
morning, crossing over into the Area from the
Eastern Perimeter. Or rather, I heard him crossing
over. He never let up* [*lifted up?]. I wouldn't have
noticed him if it weren't for the NOISE.

Thought: if this could be done in a simulated
way, then it would be an appropriate
COMMEMORATION – remembrance of the
Deliberators who first expelled the Assemblymen.
Perhaps between many Constituents, in unison?
Many insignificant works, in isolation, combining
to make one significant, indisputably! That is our
story, from that time.
    For all I ~~know~~ can Comprehend, this COULD
be how disarrangement began! The noise, barely
audible for Assemblymen as they worked, but
DEAFENING for anyone OF the Area, alert to the
noise of their thoroughfare being chewed up as
if a pulled plough was churning through it. One
person, alone, behaving normally, save for the
faintest inertia. A faint but decisive signal: there
is a movement afoot (lit.).
    But then, how to commemorate all of the rest
of the Deliberative Assembly? CONSPICUOUS
ASSOCIATION was just as necessary as the
conspicuous disarrangement that preceded it.
They are all deserving of COMMEMORATION.
    The later Assembly would be more easily
commemorated theatrically, because it was itself

more theatrical, more CONSPICUOUS. But this is not to dismiss it as less authentically Deliberative, any less deserving of commemoration. If any of it is, then it all is.

De Beauvoir Carnival. 1981

2ND FEBRUARY 2006

The wind has been stronger in the past few
days. I must be more careful on the ledge when
it's like this. RAIN is an obstruction* but it is
WIND that warrants terror. Up on the ledge I
am UNGROUNDED (lit.). My field of vision must
contain nothing that I might identify myself to be
in contact with – nothing that I am resting upon,
however indirectly. But when a strong wind
comes, this is what one looks to for assurance –
for a grounding in the world. (Terror: sense that
the world is groundless.) For now, Improvement
is as opaque as it ever was.

*RAIN – acts akin to the window opening
beneath me. The eye cannot help but track the
drops as they fall to the ground level below.
The rain brings the eye and the ground level
back into relation with one another, and any
Comprehension that comes into view falls away,
in an instant.

De Beauvoir Town. c.1971

5TH FEBRUARY 2006

There's been the clashing of Assemblymen below,
all day. Lead and steel, always in collision.
There's nothing to be seen, however.

      This was the first signal of Comprehension
– a longer duration at work (at WORK). The
second was the Centre coming into view. When
these Towers (here) are finally erected, the
Centre won't be visible. But today it was, like the
clouds clearing. This is the time for attention.
      The Centre takes on a different appearance
from this height. Unpleasant to try to put a
name to it – it cries out for a path plotted! OF
COURSE they kept it hoarded, in these early
days, before they learned to be AUTHORIAL.

The first step: a shearing action; a slight
slice. Like ~~sequiturs~~ secateurs. No – nothing
so divisive. Rather – ~~an invitation elicitation~~ an
ARRANGEMENT.

Years of disarrangement and the Area was hurrying to a Constitution that would never cohere. And if it wouldn't cohere, how would everyone (everyone!) wilfully commit to it?

The site of the Ufton Road Park (later Centre). c.1968, 1973, 1981

More thought to IMPROVEMENT prompts
memory – the COLDITZ. Before then, the
vehicles could cross the Western Perimeter
and into the Area. Over Ufton Road, over
Culford Road, over De Beauvoir Road and past
the Square, to cross the Eastern Perimeter.
Conceivably, all, with unchanging speed.

I wager, the VEHICLE is the STATIONARY
OBJECT in this scenario. The Area, by contrast:
not so much passed through, as PULLED
UNDER. As if sent through a MANGLE.

Now, afterwards, since: the vehicle follows
a passage that has been ELECTED FOR IT. 'In'
the Area no more than a finger in a ring is 'in'
precious metal. The wearer may think himself
proprietor but we'll wait some time, some
centuries, and then we'll ask him again.

Northchurch Road. 1956

Every evening, I mount the ledge, circle the perimeter, and wait for Comprehension.

I know when it is approaching, because it draws me down, towards the ground level. This, stands to reason – the Area is of a HUMAN SCALE. All of it, close to the ground level. There would be no sense in me spending time far above it.

But – the impulse continues beyond there, beyond the ground level itself.

I have considered: it is a longing. To be within the Constitution. Or, just to be rid of the winds. When there is a heavy downpour the water can collect on the flat felt for hours. And the felt pieces, usually so effective, only trap the cold rainwater against what remains of my suit, and against my bare skin. (None of this is good for morale.)

When Comprehension is at its best, the ground level can feel very close – within reach. And: ATTRACTIVE. More than once, on the ledge: a moment's nervous notice that my centre of gravity has tipped past the line of the Tower. Then a fraction of that to punch the posterior OUT, so the fall is in that direction, onto my tailbone, and not forwards, into pieces.

I can't put the INSISTENCES of the client out of mind. There is no better position for me than the one I occupy now. The reason it is so difficult to Comprehend the Improvement years can ONLY be: I haven't yet Reconstituted all of what came before.

And this leads me back to his insistences. The bald optimism of righteousness! No doubt. But I am up here, now, and he is not. However far beneath me he is, he is beneath me. He can't dominate me from where we both stand, in relation to one another.

~~But.~~

~~Still.~~

But still.

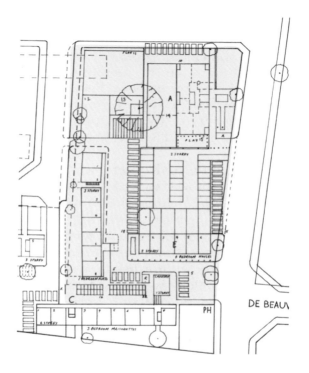

CONTINUITY. Simply: if there is continuity
in the illustration, then there was continuity
in the Assembly. If there was continuity to the
Assembly, then there was continuity to the
Deliberation. And if that is so, then it ~~may~~ will
have passed remnants into the Constitution.
And they will need to be Reconstituted.

Map referred to in the De Beauvoir Crescent Compulsory Purchase
Order 1956. 1957
De Beauvoir Town. Layout of site part 1. 17. 1964

1ST MARCH 2006

Beneath me, and close by, just beyond the ledge, everything is flat. It's all footprint – only footprint. The view from above. Further away, towards the horizon, VOLUME returns. But there, it is INDISTINCT: the capping line, the open seam; the TOP STRATA. (As it was – and, as it is!)

So, I regard this indistinct, burnt line. I suppose I don't know it so well. I suppose I wish to Reconstitute the Deliberation in its Assembly. So I imagine I go in pursuit, making passage, and I imagine I take the Solution with me. Nothing to be lost – I well know when it is having effect, as I know when it is having none.

But: I also well know what it takes, despite the ~~indistinctness~~ indistinction it has from up here, to ~~climb~~ SCALE that Assembly, that burnt line.

And I suppose I wish to EXTRACT such an Assembly, and I know – I well know – what an insurmountable demand that would be – it would not be an easy task of erasing a line! It has volume – such VOLUME! Even dis-Assembled, the Stock would cover the Area. (As it did – and, as it does!)

And then I invert this image – project it back onto the point where I am standing. And I conclude:

Whatever was here, beneath me, is still here, beneath me. No number of hands* [*dis-Assemblymen?] could remove it all. So it still remains. And anything that remains, can be recovered, and can be Reconstituted, by making a passage with the Solution, through whatever medium.

This is not SETTLING A SCORE. I am happy for that client of the Tower to live out his days wrongheaded. This is about the CONSTITUTION, and recovering all of its formative Deliberation. What there is, I will find, I will EXHUME, and I will introduce to the Solution.

Temporary road closure. c.1974

2ND MARCH 2006

Exhumation demands the right equipment, and I have none.

It is not so long ago that the Area was completed. Before that time, Deliberative Assembly could be seen everywhere, and so too could its tools.

clearing gutters and starting to move the enormous amount of rubbish still in the building.

example, but to put the allegations against Robinsons into perspective. – Ed.

Victory for diggers?

DE BEAUVOIR now has its own allotment, if only on a temporary basis. Since the idea was first suggested last Christmas, about a dozen plots have been cleared, dug over and planted out on the derelict prefab site in Ardleigh Road.

It has not been easy going, because the ground is riddled with bricks, bottles and dumped rubbish. But weather and soil conditions permitting, there should be some crops to

Planting out the peas – the Reed family from Granville Ct

tion as to when the construction of the long-awaited houses is likely to start. Even so, there is some indication that the authorities don't look unsympathetically on the principle of an allotment.

The main thing now is to work out how a permanent allotment can be set up in De Beauvoir, either on a section of one of the still derelict

These tools are exactly what I need. They are (*de facto*) IDEAL TO EXHUME the material of the Area, because that is exactly what they spent their useful lives doing, before they were necessarily retired.* [*"The shovel's handle is shaped to its owner, but its blade is shaped to its land."]

From the limited Comprehension the Solution has effected, I know who was responsible for most of this Assembly, I know where to find them, and I know where to find the tools that mediated each moment of it.

I appreciate perfectly the IRONY of combatting Extraction with Exhumation. Like my neighbours, I will displace the material of the Area, and I will begin from within my own home.

I could be descending to the level of my aggressor – IF they were identical labours, which they are NOT. They are completely dissimilar, decisively, doubly. First, the Extraction has one purpose only, and that is AUTHORIAL.

De Beaver newsletter 20. 1975
Ardleigh Road. 1975

The Exhumation stands in perfect
opposition, only DISPLACING the Constitution
(TEMPORARILY) in order to ENHANCE it. It is
INVASIVE, but only as SURGERY is. However,
because it is that, I must repair the tissue of my
subject upon exiting the corpus. I will catalogue
every piece of material removed during the
Exhumation, and I will replace it all identically
when I have recovered the obscured Deliberation
from the buried remains of Assembly.

(I have not yet devised a practicable programme
for achieving this.)

5TH MARCH 2006

Experiences remind me how attached people
can become to relics. I have paid a visit to every
Constituent (that I know of) with tools that helped
to Assemble the Area, to ask for their loan.

Some, were sceptical. That is ~~to be expected~~
right and proper. If I were in their place I would
suspect the visitor of planning a displacement
of the Constitution. And THAT IS what I am
planning! All refused, but some with reasoning
so patently fallacious: "I would loan them, but I
use them myself all the time." Etcetera. Nonsense.
Insulting! One led me to her hoard – a fine display
of armaments, dulled with a specked Gravel crust
from years of service. All in the most feeble,
failing outbuilding. No razor wire here!

6TH MARCH 2006

Yesterday: "I use them myself all the time."

Perhaps – not an INSULT, but a robust
DEFENCE of the Area?
    Everyone must know of the* [*current]
Excavation by now, and everyone must fear for
the integrity of the Constitution, because of it.

It follows: everyone must fear for whom else
might now be harbouring similar plans for
displacement. Everyone is wondering – are we
now on the way to HABITUAL Constitutional
~~abuses displacements~~ infringement? By WHOM?
Are they working IN CONCERT? And how to
IDENTIFY them? Certainly, when someone asks
to borrow one's tools of Assembly, "I use them
myself all the time" would be effective!

12TH MARCH 2006

The most disagreeable decision of the campaign,
thus far.

The Reconstitution requires tools that are well
fashioned to the Area. Anything else will scar.
That leaves only two options: find (and conspire
with) someone in ownership of such tools,
someone whose Constitutional obligations are so
lapsed they would voluntarily loan them – or, use
subterfuge, DECEIT, or even theft.

It had to be the former. In time, it will embolden the Constitution and the wrong will be annulled, but the latter is an offence that will always stand.

A SAGACIOUS decision, confirmed. An older man, today: only too happy to hand over whatever tools I could carry. Perhaps he sensed my disdain at his acquiescence, but excuses began to flow as I left: "I can't really use them myself anymore," etcetera. The most generous reading I can manage of his response is FEAR. Someone has come to his house apparently seeking the means of Extraction. One, very significant, Extraction has already been confirmed: "perhaps they have the momentum; perhaps a confrontation with Authorisers is brewing," this man may have been thinking.

Whatever. If there is any conscience that needs attention, it is his, and not mine. I have the tools I need now, and if this man's commitment to the Constitution only extends as far as keeping on the right side of a confrontation, the sooner I begin to use these tools of his, the sooner his unprincipled response to enquiries like mine will not matter.

13TH MARCH 2006

The Exhumation has begun. ~~Progress is good.~~

Progress could be better. I had planned to
dig vertically for at least three metres before
embarking south, to mitigate any RISK to the
Constitution above. I may have to be content with
~~two~~ one.

It's not possible to know the DEPTH required
to keep the Constitution above SECURE. The
Gravels are hard but once the surface is broken
with a pick, they are easily removed. The greatest
difficulty is thus not displacing material *per
se*, it is the CARE required in the cataloguing
and systematic arrangement of it in my home.
The parts cannot be reformed in an identical
relative arrangement. Nor the material put
into containers, as a vehicle for some kind of
systematised referencing shorthand. The volume
is too great.

No – the only resolution is a MENTAL
CATALOGUE. I am still rising to* [*fathoming?]
this challenge, but it is at least a distraction
from the extreme PHYSICAL demands (and
excellent COMPREHENSIVE UNDERGIRDING).
Rather than burdening the mind with abstract,
mediating denotation, I am required to establish
and maintain familiarity only and directly with
the material itself. (The Constitution, deep under
the nails and deep under the skin!)

The upshot is, visual phenomena are of no
use (at best a DISTRACTION), and I have taken
to working without any light, at all. Rather than

learning to identify a referencing system, I am
learning to identify peculiarities of density, odour,
inhabitation (in the case of one ants nest) and
composition – humus, and so forth. The extended
funnel* [*(worm)cast?] that is growing up around
me each day is composed of the material that
will itself, when this work is over, when the
Exhumation is complete, provide the script to
execute the same process, but in reverse.

11TH APRIL 2006

I have never been of such a BULK! A day now is
as physically demanding as any day can be. I am
wary of sharpening any of the shovels and picks,
in case their owner realises how INTENSIVELY
they have been used. So I continue with blunted
blades and imperfect points.

(As well: the rain, wind and cold of the Tower are
almost appealing against the air and heat at this
level. SUFFOCATING.)

If the advance is precarious PHYSICALLY, then
so too is it GEOGRAPHICALLY. Landmarks*
[*lit.] are invaluable for establishing distance –
no TRIANGULATION is possible between points
only experienced in sequence. Best of all are tree
roots, corroborating my location, down here, to
a familiar position in the Constitution, above.
But: because they MEDIATE so between the two
spheres, it could not be more important to avoid

damage to a root structure that would injure the upper part of the tree. As a consequence, my plotted path has been compromised several times.*

[*It offends everything I know to cross the Area (to CROSS the Area) this way. An ARBITRARY route (root?), taking no heed of the Assembly, or of the myriad Deliberations that formed it. I put out of mind what an illustration of my path would resemble. A drunken tail of jasmine, flailing aimlessly?]

The largest structures set progress back by several DAYS. I have adjusted my trajectory to keep well away from the Square.

20TH JUNE 2006

I have arrived at the Southern Extraction.

There is no ~~catharsis~~ ~~liberation~~ EUPHORIA. Landmark root structures have brought ~~a measured~~ an only incremental advance, and an only incremental success.

  Some PRIDE, all the same. No other person has even attempted what I have, I am sure. (To qualify: there have been a great many rightful (Deliberative) displacements – easily identified, upon a transition from the Gravels to something far softer, as immediate as one throw of the pick from the next.)

In any case, I am here now, and my arrival has already been greeted with the BLUNT HOSTILITY of concrete foundations extending (Authorised!) in every direction. No easier for a pick than for the Solution. I will change course to go around.

1ST JULY 2006

The concrete is interminable.

INTERMINABLE.

I pause working all the time – from INDIGNATION, not exhaustion. Two days ago, I destroyed a shovel out of IRE. I watched my right hand throw it blade-on against the concrete face. With nothing to dampen the impact from either blade or concrete, the force transferred up the metalwork, to the pin that should secure it to the wooden shaft, but which now, in an instant, was splitting its grain up the entire length. I don't know how I will explain this to the owner.

What buries all of my patience is not the HOSTILITY of the material but its ORDER OF MAGNITUDE.* Of late, it is all overwhelming. My concern now – the success of the Solution is being undone. To reason: I have aligned my body with the Deliberators. I have formed my hands (my gait) to their tools. In doing so, I may have revived a PARITY OF SCALE between myself and them. (This would explain it.)

[*'Order of Magnitude': a newly encountered Order is always SINCERELY CONFOUNDING. If it could be anticipated from a familiar Order then they would bear EQUIVALENCE and the term would be meaningless!]

4TH JULY 2006

Necessity is the mother of invention, but reason is its midwife: the concrete can be OVERCOME.

First, bury the butt of the pick handle in the ground – in the Gravels. Only a few centimetres are needed, sufficient for the pick to stand of its own, with only the point resting square-on against the concrete face. Next: LAUNCH an iron hammer against the butt of the blade, to send its point HARD into the face its point rests against.

It will prompt a chip, but later a fissure, and then a crack, growing until concrete pieces begin to FALL AWAY. (The RELISH in tossing them aside – no cataloguing needed for this assembly!) When the steel reinforcements are revealed, they are easily forced to one side.

The triumph has sped my pace – I hope to be through by tomorrow.

5TH JULY 2006

If I do not have the capacity to render intelligible all that is now before me, then I at least do to know that this is the case. For now, I should record only the events of the past ~~12~~ ~~24~~ 48 hours, as they have occurred.

Hammering through concrete is loud. I had been finishing well before daybreak, out of caution. Assuming (correctly) that the steel reinforcements run through the centre of the material, I was two hours from penetrating the farther face.

It was then about that long before daybreak. The disappointment would have been crushing, but for the exhaustion. I pulled my blankets around me, fell into my mal-formed niche and slept, there and then. Later: woke, resumed – and the remaining depth fell away.

BUT.

When the final, decisive moment came, it was not met with the GRIT-SCRAPE of more Gravels (liberated from compaction!) but with the TIN-CLANG of sheet steel.

NO CHANGE as the aperture widened. Early strikes punctured a hole in the sheet but later it only flexed. So – clearly not a laminate affixed to the concrete. Nor even, trapped between the concrete and more Gravels behind. (Though it may as well have been, for the inertia of it.) But it could be moved – small increments only,* but enough to confirm OPEN SPACE on the other side [*tilt – like an opening door?]. I dropped a piece of concrete through the opening, as depth gauge. Conclusion: a surface below about level with the one I have made for myself.

I had thought the air in my corridor was stale. From this aperture came something far worse. Stale but also leaden. None of the HUMIDITY that gives my corridor its sharper edge.

I will not pretend none of this perturbed. But: my objective for so long has been to overcome an obstacle that had represented itself to me as UNASSAILABLE. All of my work to this point had BANISHED that. To turn back out of fear would be to reinstate it.

But: climbing through feet-first would have been sensible. The distance to the floor on the other side was greater than I had estimated. My JAW was to confirm it. The difference was less than a metre, but that was enough for my centre of gravity to move BEYOND the concrete (hitherto beneath it) before my hands could extend to the ground below to break my fall (rather than my shoulder, cranium, vertebrae – or jaw).

(Digressing. Only to add: the mouthful of blood soon dried and the only tooth lost had been causing me pain for many months.)

So the ground here was hard, at least. And SYNTHETIC, from the frictionless smear that became of the blood.

The steel is not a sheet but an oblong. With an open front. With SHELVING. With FILES – box, loose, bound, tied. MORE, I could feel to either side. MORE, continuing along the wall, in both directions, following round to the adjacent walls, at either end, and opposite.

I went to fetch a torch.

(Before the conclusion: I have had time to consider its worth – credible, irresistible, or absurd. It is all of these things, just as this reflection upon it is. It is all too much, with lacerated clothes and a newly arranged mouth.)

The space on the other side is a vault HOLD and its contents are AUTHORIAL.

Area of order land – 10·896 acres gross.
There are about 159 houses, 7 factories, a block of shops
& flats, a warehouse, public house, stables, garage
etc. in the order. With some exceptions the
dwellings are about 100 years old.

Soon enough: daybreak approaching. I will return tomorrow. Climbing back through the aperture (FEET first) I took care to pull the shelving unit into its original position using my pick-hole, in case this vault is ever patrolled. The original motion was much easier in reverse, no doubt helped by the newly lubricated floor beneath.

Ministry of Housing and Local Government internal memo:
De Beauvoir Town CPO 1959. 1961

7TH JULY 2006

Whatever is held in the Hold, whatever it is, is DEAFENING.

The resistance of the concrete under compression, I admired from the outside. Its resistance under tension, I admire now from the inside. There is ~~FEVER~~ FERVOUR in the stacks, though their contents defer to their aggregated, material orderliness (thank goodness, or I would have no chance).

It is all of a FORCE. But there is no sophistication to that force, only a RELENTLESS AGGREGATION. Whose methods are these at work? 'Stacks' is too appropriate!

The first bafflement is why they are here at all. The second is, what from among them can be ~~expropriated~~ expatriated for my own use?

To the first question, I answer: the Hold is supremely AUTHORIAL: the steel stacks, the dismal order, the stubborn concrete (IMPERVIOUS to the Solution), the arid air (discomforting cool).

To the second question, I can only say for now that I advance cautiously. Aside from my ~~hysteria~~ troubles on the night of breakthrough, I have left no trace of my visits. I remove sheets from files, but only ones that I am sure, from their pristine condition, will not be missed. (I have not found any that could be described otherwise.)

9TH JULY 2006

This is DELIBERATION here, but not as I had
expected to find it. It is all of a PIECE – and
none of those pieces, assembled together with
any other. But when it is all taken as it is, in
pieces, one after another, in turn, then it takes
on a familiar appearance. A consoling warmth
in this dark place!

An Authorisation was made, of TOTAL
EXTRACTION, amidst cohering common
ASSOCIATION, amidst DISARRANGED
ASSEMBLY. A VISITING AUTHORISER came
and was sent away, reoriented by the FORCE OF
ASSOCIATION. I have checked and rechecked
the dates. This is all as it was in 1972, but this
is 1959:

> "I WAS INVITED BY THE DE BEAUVOIR
> TOWN RESIDENTS' ASSOCIATION
> TO INSPECT THE INTERIOR OF
> THE DWELLINGS AND I DID SO IN A
> NUMBER OF CASES.
>
> MULTIPLE OCCUPATION CAN LEAD TO
> SERIOUS NEGLECT AND DEPRECIATION
> OF THE FABRIC OF DWELLINGS BUT
> I FOUND LITTLE EVIDENCE OF THIS
> IN THE HOUSES I INSPECTED AND I
> WAS IMPRESSED BY THE EFFORTS OF
> OWNER/OCCUPIERS AND OTHERS TO
> IMPROVE THEIR ACCOMMODATION.

HAVING REGARD TO THE WEIGHT OF OBJECTION AND THE TYPE OF STRUCTURAL CONDITION OF THE HOUSES, I CONSIDER THAT AN OPPORTUNITY SHOULD BE GIVEN TO IMPROVE THEM."

After this point, I still struggle.

The De-Beauvoir Town Residents Association.

Benyon Rd,
London
N.1.

Ref. HSB2/724/219 and -/168.
Housing Act 1957.
The De-Beauvoir Town C.P.O. 1959.

11/12/60.

Letter from 20 Benyon Road to the Minister of Housing
and Local Government. 1960

14TH JULY 2006

A ~~disaster derailment diversion~~ divergence.

Housing Acts, 1936 to 1952 and the
Acquisition of Land (Authorisation Procedure) Act, 1946

................*De Beauvoir Town*................(C.P.O.) 1959

Mr. ....*Ron*.............

L. 1 & (B) L 1(A)

The above named C.P.O. has been made under Part V of the
Housing Act, 1936, and submitted for confirmation.

A copy of the Order and a copy of the Map (both of which
should be returned) showing the land in the Order are attached.

Will you please return this form with your comments as soon
as possible. If we do not hear from you by .... it
will be assumed that you have no comments to offer and our action on
the order will proceed.

Division/*(A)*, Rm. ....*35 III Wh1.*........

........*23/2/60*..Date

533|00
183|90

OVER

***

✱ Delete where necessary.

Here, Authorisation was followed through. The visiting Authoriser was well Peered, but after that time, in the Hold, it is grave. When Association speaks, it is not at all Authorial.* [*"ON BEHALF OF MY ASSOCIATION MEMBERS, I AM WRITING TO ENQUIRE AS TO WHEN YOU ARE LIKELY TO MAKE A DECISION IN REGARD TO THE ABOVE ORDER."] If I can see that, he would have had no difficulty distinguishing his own works from those of Deliberators, which he directed straight into the Hold, severed from Assembly. No surveying, no Comprehension, no Centre, no Authorial path plotted, all as their counterparts in the Area would do, a decade later.

I feel unfit, unwell. Being in the Hold, it's an otolithic ado. Navigating forwards as always, but with the senses only recording stasis. HERE ARE THE SPOILS! I have learned all I need to from this place.

XXXXXXXXXXXXX
COVent Garden 0271
Extn. 3733

≤1 SEP 1961

Sir,

Housing Act, 1957 and Acquisition of Land (Authorisation Procedure) Act, 1946 De Beauvoir Town Compulsory Purchase Order 1959

I am directed by the Minister of Housing and Local Government to enclose the above Order which the Minister has confirmed without modification, together with the sealed map referred to therein for deposit in the offices of the Council.

I also enclose a copy of a letter addressed to the objectors.

I am to request that six copies of the Order as confirmed may be forwarded to the Department for official use as soon as possible. No attestation clauses need be reproduced. The copies should bear a heading in the following terms:-

"Copy of the De Beauvoir Town Compulsory Purchase Order, 1959, as confirmed without modification by the Minister of Housing and Local Government on the 1st day of September 1961."

/A

Submission for Ministry of Housing and Local Government
confirmation of De Beauvoir Town CPO 1959. 1960
Ministry of Housing and Local Government confirmation
of De Beauvoir Town CPO 1959. 1961

For now, I have the advantage. I am quite sure no one knows of my discovery, and it must stay that way.*

The Deliberation of the Hold is LIBERATED: I have DRAINED the relevant files and replaced their contents with blank sheets so the stacks still keep the Hold under tension, as they did before. The Hold is SEALED, with the same wretched concrete I picked away. And, I begin the necessary task of replacing the Gravels in their original locations. It is not so difficult. I lived with them for many weeks, but they seem to know their rightful place even better than I do.

VIGILANCE is more important than ever – all of the time I executed this process in reverse, I was unknowingly building passage for myself into the Authorisers' security safe, that they have ~~done~~ assembled so much to OBSCURE – to DISTRACT ATTENTIONS from.

*That said: soon after returning from the Hold yesterday morning, I was alerted by the long shadows of first light to two Authorisers (I am CERTAIN) standing close to my house, just beyond my walls. They stood for some time, looking down at the ground level, at a point DIRECTLY above the route of my passage below. Impressing footprints (in an impression?) – making gestures like the CONCAVITY of a COPPER!

23RD JULY 2006

Sitting by the window, for as long as I am able,
at a time (eyes still adjusting after these many
weeks). Outside, the Authorisers have returned,
several times. Their confidence GROWS, I
can see. Petty intimidation is all it is, beneath
contempt.* [*beneath, contempt?]
    The HOLD is the object of concern. It has
held the frayed ends of Deliberation that I knew
I would find, but not in the form I expected
to find them. It must be reintroduced into the
Assembly – it must REPOPULATE it. It has been
occluded since its time, in parallel and severance
from the Association (the SECOND Association!),
the Improvement, and the Completion. The
Reconstitution will not be a TRANSFER of the
Constitution; it will be an IMPROVEMENT of it.
IMPROVEMENT MUST RECOMMENCE!

25TH JULY 2006

EL HIERRO: THE IRON!

This: this is the Solution.

The Towers – these edifices, beset with iron
lattices, waiting (WEIGHTING) – demanding a
comparison to that island be drawn (illustrated?).
They will become our RESOURCE, our
ASSOCIATIVE FORCE EXPRESSED, and
IMPRESSING! There will be no more Peering,
no more shadow play, no more use for the

resources of any Authoriser. Deliberation, resurrected, re-Assembled.

Uncommitted Constituents will find themselves MAROONED! Their Authorial tempters, nowhere in sight. All around them, Deliberators returning their tools to use, sharpening blunted blades, polishing dulled faces, holding them aloft, for RECONSTITUTION!

The Towers were built to their EXTREME HEIGHT to obscure what I have now discovered, and EXACTLY THIS will now be put to work AGAINST their Authors.

Each Tower collects water on its roof, and each distributes it down, to the ground level below. This will be REVERSED, without betraying any sign of it. The EXPOSURE at the height of the Tower brings winds enough to take the water that collects in the open spaces around it to the ROOF, where the height of the ledge will comfortably barricade water up to waist height. One WIND TURBINE will be positioned at the centre of the cistern capping each Tower, at a height no greater than the line of sight to that point from the ground level below. Its trunk will thus stand in the stored water, and so will also contain the ballcock to regulate water storage. Lest we awake one autumn day to a twenty storey fountain – a waterfall on all sides!

The pinholes, the arterioles – they must all be PLUGGED. Any opening overlooked is a FISSURE that will allow DISARRANGEMENT back in – it will allow the noxious VAPOURS to come up through the cracks to massage our purpose into gentle submission, once again.

The water will transport, up and down, through the existing guttering (drainage) system, and this will also need to be SECURED, entirely, for the same reasons. The bricks, their APOROSITY, and that concrete – any run-off will STAIN, ~~brickly~~ briskly. We may as well announce our Reconstitution with FLARES! (Those chutes, the protruding pipes, at the peak for their fetid-green stain-spray: always a spectacle – a COMET atop its tail!)

When we need to call on our resource, the water will be released back through the system, EXCITING GENERATION as it goes. Until then, it will be our RESERVE – our RESERVOIR!

There will be no indication of any of this from the ground level. The turbines, the channels, the reservoirs – yes, they will be seen, but only from their equivalent positions on the other Towers. The rest is only a reversal of flows, purpose, utility and BIDDING.

As the water begins to circulate, so too will the newly liberated Deliberation, repatriated with the ~~assembly~~ Assembly. It will effect what it should have done so many years before: an AUTHORIAL PATH PLOTTED in this RECONSTITUTED AREA.

8TH AUGUST 2006

The URGENCY! The promise of Deliberative
Assembly to one side, the threat of Authorisers,
to the other. Every day now, I see them, beyond
my walls, in NUMBERS. The Gravels are
almost all replaced. Yesterday: commencing
work before nightfall, to speed ~~completion~~
replacement along. Men circling overhead, I
am sure of it. Loose roots shuddering. Murmur.
Smothered heels. Knocking.

RELATED ACCOUNTS

Transcriber's Note

The texts are edited from accounts related throughout 2015. Each person was either directly involved in, or is in some other way associated with, the localised collective action that was prominent in De Beauvoir between 1968 and the mid-1980s.

Each account was related in normal conversation and then transcribed from a recording. Paragraphs, sentences and words were then altered and repositioned for coherence and brevity. The respective relater was invited to alter their text further if they wished to; most made minor amendments and a few rewrote their account entirely, though covering roughly the same subjects as before. The texts have not been 'fact-checked' and no claims or opinions were challenged.

Only Robin Simpson lived outside of De Beauvoir Town in the period concerned. His account was related to Dominic Simpson, who prepared the transcription prior to editing.

The interspersed images have been positioned close to a relevant passage of text, though they do not necessarily relate to the relater any more closely than this. Images have been captioned only where there are more details to offer than those in the image itself.

J.H.

JEREMY HORNSBY and *JAY HORNSBY*

One day, somebody said to me, Jeremy, could you do me a favour, I've got something to be delivered over to De Beauvoir, and you've got a car, and I haven't. I said 'where's De Beauvoir?' and of course it was only half a mile away. I'd never heard of it. So I came to this wonderful place – wonderful houses and trees – and half the houses were empty. You could literally walk into them, because they'd been abandoned. All across De Beauvoir. I climbed into many of them myself.

...

Frank Fletcher was the curator of the British Museum catalogue, and to the best of my knowledge, it was Frank that dreamed up the De Beauvoir Association. A lot of other people later claimed glory for it, but Frank was quite a mild, humble sort of person.

He started writing to the council as if he was the leader of 10,000 men, when actually, it was just him and his wife and his dog. So eventually the council stopped their shenanigans and it wasn't demolished. But of course, half of the houses were still empty.

Frank lived just over the road, and next door to us was Mrs Honeybourne. That house was worse than mine. Absolutely awful. She lived there with her daughter and her brother, who was a night watchman. They didn't even have an inside loo. They had no hot water in the house.

...

It was in '73, and I would say that I was one of the first. There was Frank Fletcher – you'd call him a professional person – and Robin Young and Stuart Weir, but there were not many. As I say, half the houses were empty. It was probably towards the end of the '70s that the real difference came, when people started coming in. That was when the council finally lifted the planning blight. The escalation was very rapid.

I met Stuart Weir and Robin Young once or twice; I wouldn't say I knew them. I met them at DBA meetings and things. And also, when we did up the old WRVS building off Culford Road, where they later built all those council houses – too many houses in the space, breaking their own regulations. It's a strange shame that they lost it.

The Ufton Centre, it was lovely – it was in a small field. You went in and across the grass, and then this long low brick building, two storeys. It had been WRVS, making socks and things for the lads during the war. Of course, it was total chaos and we spent two whole days clearing the whole thing out.

I wasn't heavily involved, but I was a helper. I was incredibly busy then, I was working very hard, and I just didn't have the time to go to committee meetings and things, and I was trying to do up the house, which was taking every bit of my money. I thought it would take me five years but it took me ten.

...

Some of the old-fashioned people, it wasn't like a village thing for them. They tended not to talk to

NEW DEVELOPMENT BY
RYDER ASSOCIATES
REFLECTING
BOTH
NEW &
OLD
DE
BEAUVOIR
TOWN

74
TO BE REDEVELOPED

RESERVED
AREA

BIG CHIEF FRANK FLETCHER.

each other too much. A native East End wariness, I suppose. There was John the postman who lived next door with his wife who worked down the road making those snap-together filing things. He was a very right-wing little chap. Their garden was surrounded by the printers. It's now been demolished and Mr Benyon has built a lot of little bijou houses there.

He, as far as I can recall, had nothing to do with trying to save De Beauvoir. Of course, what he had done was he'd sold all the leases. He thought it was all going to be pulled down so he thought 'I know, I'm going to be smart – I'll sell all these leases, because then I'll make all the money'. But of course, now they're trying to buy all the leases back because he realised the family had made a terrible mistake.

...

Do you remember that man, that nice man that helped us in the garden – John. His family had lived in Ufton Road for years and they went to Hereford.

I helped him plant trees in De Beauvoir, yes. He was a very nice guy, very knowledgeable.

He said, 'everyone is moving out; all our friends have gone'. He must have been quite late doing it. There was a sort of mass exodus in the '70s – we saw him in '81 but then he moved. He said, 'it's just got so rough round here' – because when Jeremy moved us, it was.
John told me 'we're still here, but everyone's going, because the area isn't what it was'. They were all very respectable. Nobody signed off from school.

It was extremely respectable. They all knew each other, and the children behaved.

What they were was upper working class. That's how they would be described. Which is that very particular thing – exactly as you say, very respectable. Not necessarily aspiring middle class, but they were the top of the working class ladder. There would be no nicking.

...

The guy over the other side of the road, he had a rented house but he was trying to do it up as much as possible. He was installing a bar in it. It was very funny because the Greeks had put all this real crap in my house and I was taking it out and putting it in the skip and he was taking out all the nice old bits from his house, the sort of thing that I would covet, which I was then rescuing from the skip, while he was rescuing the horrible modern bits that I was taking out. I thought I'd write a play about this one day. It would make a wonderful play called *The Skip* – you know, the interchange of social attitudes.

REMINDER !

* As a resident of the Southern Area you can write to the Minister of the Environment and tell him what you want to see happen in the area.

- Do you want the Improvement Area retained or rescinded?

- Do you want to continue to live in the area?

- Do you want better conditions?

Whatever **your** point of view **write** to the Minister

Letters should be sent to:

The Secretary,
Department of the Environment,
Caxton House,
Tothill Street,
London, SW1 H9LZ.

and **must** arrive by <u>10th March, 1972</u>.

URGENT

MICHAEL EDWARDS

I didn't get heavily involved in the local politics of the area, except for little episodes. The earliest was around 1970, when I first went to be a teacher at UCL. I found myself working with a group of half-a-dozen planning students who were interested in studying the area, and got into an alliance with the Southern Area Action Group, who were the people living in the next strip of housing north of the New Town Estate, campaigning for improvement and against demolition. As far as I recall, they were mostly either tenants or leaseholders of the Benyon family. The Benyon family had a long and terrible history of never investing in the properties they owned. They were just milking it for rent and never investing back into it, and it was in extraordinarily bad condition. It was an extremely decayed set of buildings.

It seems to me in a way that De Beauvoir is very much a microcosm of things that were going on all over the place in London. The one that caught all the attention is the Packington Street Estate. There was a huge public inquiry about that which was very pivotal in marshalling the arguments to say, well, the endless bulldozing of terraced houses and streets in London needs to stop, or slow down, and these buildings could be conserved, repaired, and brought back into use. That was just about the moment when the power turned in terms of policy and fashion and prevailing practices. So the De Beauvoir pattern was just one of twenty or thirty or fifty campaigns like that going on in London at that time, and it felt very good to win it.

The area got declared to be an improvement area and became eligible for government grants to upgrade housing, which could be claimed by owner-occupiers or landlords, but not by tenants. That mechanism became a really rather important ingredient in areas like this because it was strongly in the interests of estate agents and speculators and individual families to try to get tenants out of housing, buy them, do them up, benefit from the government grants and end up with a really nice house rather cheaply, which is what was happening. And I think it was happening pretty uniformly through the '70s and '80s in pretty much the whole of the De Beauvoir area.

...

I never really studied the area but, to me, it's always seemed that to make sense of De Beauvoir Town you have to go back a very long way, to its original development. As far as I recall, the original developer of this land, from agricultural land to housing, got the site very cheap.

Perhaps it was that which enabled them to build it out at this extremely low density, with the rather gracious arrangement of this grid of streets, with these diagonal ones, and with the square – a really quite luxurious layout, when undoubtedly they could have made a lot more money by building at the kind of densities you find just across Southgate Road, which must be at least double. It left an inheritance of this land as not very intensively used, but with rather lovely – potentially lovely – space including gardens.

DO COME

PUBLIC MEETING
THUR 8·00 CRYPT

STOP PRESS.......STOP PRESS......STOP PRESS. ....

LAT ST NEWS!

THE COUNCIL AND THEIR OFFICERS HAVE DRAWN UP PLANS FOR THE
SOUTHERN AREA OF DE BEAUVOIR TOWN THAT IS THE PART IN WHICH
YOU LIVE. THEY ARE GOING TO HOLD A MEETING IN THE CRYPT OF
ST PETER'S CHURCH, DE BEAUVOIR SQARE AT 8 O'CLOCK ON THURSDAY
APRIL 15th. SO THAT WE CAN DISCUSS THEM BEFORE THEY GO TO
THE HOUSING COMMITTEE.

LET'S HEAR WHAT THEY HAVE TO SAY, AND HOW FAR THEIR PROPOSALS
MATCH UP TO YOUR OWN NEED, HOW THEY ANSWER THE DEMANDS IN THE
S.I.A.G. REPORT AND THE QUESTIONS ON THE NEWS SHEET WHICH YOU
HAD DELIVERED THIS WEEK- END

THIS IS THE MOST IMPORTANT PUBLIC MEETING SO FAR HELD FOR THE
SOUTHERN AREA.

PLEASE COME.

...

The area had really a lot of industry. It had a lot of scattered small workshops, a few of which remain, but most of which don't. My brother-in-law bought one of them – it was a workshop in the back end of somebody's garden that had been built sometime in the 19th century. He used that as a furniture making workshop for 15 years, very successfully.

In the next-door garden there was a similar workshop that was used by a zinc smelter – a rather old man who would make castings out of zinc. I can't remember what they were for, but that's what he did. I think he was doing alloys with lead and other metals. The smell was terrible and we always suspected it was very toxic. There were a lot of other small industries in the area. There was still instrument making – scientific instrument making.

...

It wasn't until after working on the Southern Area that I came to live here, in Buckingham Road. It was a pair of houses – one of those semi-detached pairs of houses. The first had been bought a few years earlier by a friend and then the one next door came up for sale. Another friend's mother had been widowed so she had the proceeds from a semi-detached house in Huddersfield, which was enough to buy this very crumbly house in Buckingham Road.

So these two houses were merged into a single unit – we were setting up a commune, in the spirit of the women's movement in the '70s. We initially had about seven or eight people in these two houses and then more people came and joined and we managed to get the next house. An elderly couple had been living there – this was very typical of the area in the '70s – in a reducing part of the building, because the damp was so terrible. The top floor was quite unusable because of the leaking roof and the top floor had buckets and tin baths and things to collect the rain from the leaking roof. The floor below that had a lot of mildew and rot and it was really only the ground floor that they were able to use. So that was really very difficult. They died and the house was on the market and we bought it – I can't remember for how much, but not a lot, because it was in such a ruinous state. So then we had three.

We built a new building in between two of them and extended out a large kitchen and living room area to the back, which meant getting planning permission from the council, who couldn't decide whether it should be classified as residential or not. In the end we got planning permission that was called 'suis generis (commune)'. The neighbours, initially, were very frightened because they had letters from the council saying there is a proposal to open a commune in their street. We went to talk to them and they said 'oh, it's just you!' and withdrew their objections.

C. INDUSTRY & COMMERCE

4.38 **INDUSTRY IN THE AREA :**

The table below gives some indication of the variety of size and type of industry to be found in the area : (I)

NAME	TENURE	SIZE	TYPE	NO. OF EMPLOYEES	NO. LOCAL.	SHIFTS
E. Machin			bridal headwear	6 women	6	1
Precious Baby Products	T	1,000 sq.ft.	baby products and nursery furniture.	5	4	1
Leader & Arbus.	T	2 floors	mantles & costumes.	3	-	1
A. Calton & Sons.	L.H.	large	bakery	10	-	2: 10-6 6-2
Klinger Boxes	L.H.	5000 sq.ft.	mfr. cardboard boxes.	-	-	1
L. Marcus	-	-	furniture mfr.	-	-	-
Jenkins.	L.H.	6000 sq.ft.	Sawdust mfr.	20	-	1
Downham Supplies	-	-	supplies contractors tools.	-	-	-
Circle Car Hire	-	-	car hire & workshops.	-	-	-
Godfrey Jacques & Co.	-	-	turf accountants	-	-	-

Contd.

JOAN MILLER

The committee meetings were held at the town hall. My husband, Stan, was chairman of the steering committee for the area, to stop the houses being pulled down and leave things as they were. There used to be sparks flying because, although it was Conservative, there were also a lot of Labour people who were councillors. When the Conservatives got in it was a big surprise, but Labour were bully-boys.

Although Stan wasn't on the council, he was a member of the public that they chose to help form their views on what should be done with the area. He and the lady who owned the bar fitting place, and Mabel Hall. She, Lou and Stan would go off to the meetings together.

...

We were all delighted, those that didn't want it to be destroyed. The old houses were becoming dilapidated because there were rumours about what the council was going to do. Nobody was buying, nobody was selling and nobody was bothering to do up their houses. It was all mod cons on the new estate. You had a bathroom – it was a palace, compared to how things were going in the houses.

When it really got serious, Benyon himself and the members of the community got together and said, 'we'll try and fight this because they are solid houses; alright, they need a bit of tarting up now, but they are solid and they are worth saving'. It was a mad rush to get the houses properly habitable for tenants.

The area now is wonderful, but I don't think anyone ever could have imagined it being as it is. Not as it was. When they were doing this house up, we came round to have a look, and the house next door had a huge union jack painted on the front door and there were squatters in there. People were moving out and leaving their homes because it was all going to be pulled down, anyway. They moved out and the squatters moved in.

Those that had been there for years looked after their property. They were leaseholders – who were looking after it better than the odd landlord that was dotted around – and they were fighting to keep it as it is.

As far as I was know, there was no organised march or anything like that. You didn't show your displeasure like that in those days. It was just paperwork and committee meetings, arguing the toss.

...

We moved here from our first house in De Beauvoir in '72, when they started to put the barriers up at the end of the road. Before then, around the corner, we had four rooms. They wanted to do it up, but in order to do so, they needed us out. This house at the time was being renovated, and the Benyon Estate manager, Barry Brown, said to us, 'there's a house around the corner that's being renovated, it's eight rooms' – because I'd had three children – 'and you can use them as you like'.

This was the first house with an indoor toilet and bathroom I ever lived in. We had a copper when we

Name of Firm	Address	Type of Business
S.Endleman & Son.Ltd.	129, Balls Pond Road	Millinery manufacture
Monarch Silversmiths Ltd.	143, Balls Pond Road	Silversmiths,electro-platers
H.Moss Jnr.	159/161, Balls Pond Road	Trowel good manufacturers
Awool Insulation Ltd.	167, Balls Pond Road	Insulation manufacturers
T & S. Automatic Springs	1, Culford Mews.	Building Engineers
Dag Motors Ltd.	7, Culford Mews	Taxi repairs
Wood Handrail Co.Ltd.	163 & 167, Culford Road	Joinery manufacture
Romulus Engineers Co.Ltd.	152A, Totenham Road	Mech. & elec. engineering
Pardit Bros.Ltd.	155, Balls Pond Road	Clothing manufacture
H & B.Becker	167/171, Balls Pond Road	Dressmaking
M & E.Cooper	169/171, Balls Pond Road	Dress manufacture
Atlantis Garages (Islington) Ltd.	85, Balls Pond Road	Motor repairs
Stanmore Springs Ltd.	98/100, Tottenham Road (and 6-16 Arbutus Street)	Manufacturers of floor Springs
Jersey Knitting Co.Ltd.	47A, Balls Pond Road	Knitted Fabric Manufacture

moved into our first house in De Beauvoir. It was a little brick outbuilding and it covered a copper bowl, or a zinc bowl with a brick trim around it. There was a space underneath where you lit the fire to boil the water that you put in the bowl to do the washing. You had a scullery one side of the garden and a toilet on the other. They all went in the '70s renovations.

And this house was the first occupation that we didn't have to share with anyone. Even the house in Limehouse, as a child, was shared; my mother let a bedroom to a young couple with a baby.

...

The De Beauvoir Association had a lot of skills – architects, solicitors, lawyers. They naturally owned their houses – leasehold, because the freehold didn't come into effect until after the conservation area. The government told the landlords that if the people wanted to buy the freeholds, and they had the money to, then they could. Those that were lawyers, doctors – those that had the money – were able to. But we weren't in the money like that. At that point, Stan was a house-to-house book salesman. I worked at De Beauvoir School from 1970 until I retired at 64, working up from dinner lady to secretary. Later on, the headmaster set up a new school in Moorgate and asked me to come out of retirement and I worked there part-time for another 12 years.

...

There was a factory in Ufton Grove that made plaster models of wedding cake pillars and Father Christmases, ranging from 2 inches to 4 inches. I would paint them to make extra money. Red clothes, black boots, pink face. Dot the eyes and make a mouth. I was a home worker, so I would go to collect them, but there were a lot of outdoor workers, all painting these little figures, and others working with the moulds.

It was my brother-in-law's business. He knocked a hole in the wall between him and the next house to use the two as his business. That rather upset the neighbour, and the deliveries of plaster and machinery. He bought our first house in De Beauvoir for mum and me and my other sister, and kept a workshop next door with a metalwork lathe to make birthday candle holders. You couldn't get sugar to make the proper ones because it was war time, so he made them out of metal. You had to stamp the flower and twist it on the spiral.

Tenants Action

We have had two deputations to the Town Hall about tenants' poor living conditions and harassment by landlords. Hackney Council has promised to use its powers

- to make landlords put tenanted homes into decent repair -- and to get rid of DAMP

- to make landlords put in lavatories, baths, hot and cold water, etc, into tenanted homes which lack these basic amenities

- to take into Council ownership (by compulsory purchase if necessary) any property where the landlord harasses tenants or unfairly gives them NOTICE TO QUIT

- to check on offers of poor alternative accommodation to tenants who are asked to move to allow their homes to be improved

BUT WE MUST KEEP THE PRESSURE UP. We must make sure that homes are improved for tenants and not for sale to newcomers to the area. How long have YOU been waiting for a decent home ? Come and tell us what you want -- so we can tell the Council. And help us plan our next move . . .

Come to a tenants´ meeting at 8.00pm

on THURSDAY MAY 10

at St PETER'S CHURCH CRYPT
Northchurch Rd N1

A DE BEAUVOIR ASSOCIATION MEETING

STUART WEIR

I moved to De Beauvoir knowing very little about it at all – it was a house, only. But I was very interested in public participation in housing matters and the Skeffington Report, and so on. I started doing some general campaigning work and realised that the council had a rolling programme of demolition that had already started, and that the whole of De Beauvoir was due to be demolished. Robin and I decided we'd launch a campaign, so we did.

We'd been in the Liberal party after Orpington, and we had the idea that people count. So we were both populists, in the proper sense of the word, and we knew about election campaigning. We decided we would go around with a megaphone and tell people about this meeting coming up in the crypt of the church.

At the meeting, I was talking to the Labour councillor for the district – who didn't live in De Beauvoir, of course. Only a trickle of people were coming in, and he said, 'people are far too apathetic, they don't come to meetings'. Then suddenly, about 200 people flooded in and we had a rousing meeting. It was very exciting. People were angry and they expressed that. So I said, let's come back in two weeks' time and set up the Association.

We moved very, very fast. Someone said, 'oh we must have an election', and I said, no, anybody who wants to be on the committee should just come along and be a member. I felt sure that if you had elections lots of people who could contribute would just drop out straight away – it doesn't go with the psyche. I think we had about 30 or so people come along, sometimes more. They were self-elected – the idea being that anybody who wanted to contribute should contribute.

I remember Mrs Hall and her sister said they wanted to do something for the old folk. I said, 'great, come along and we'll do something'. They must have been in their sixties or seventies themselves. So it wasn't overly formal. We had a constitution of sorts, which I wrote, I think. At the committee meetings we said we wouldn't have one or two people dominating, so when we were discussing an issue, we'd go around so everybody would have a chance to speak. Very often it's a few people with very clear views who get ahead, and often that's a question of class and I didn't want it to become middle class dominated. Of course it was middle class dominated in a sense, because I'm middle class and I was a very dominant figure at the beginning.

We made a well-known local Conservative the vice chair of our committee – a horrible man. He was, in a sense, against lots of the things we were saying and doing. But we made him vice chair with deliberate intent, because we wanted to be non-party political and we obviously had to be.

I was chair for two years and then I stopped. One of my rules, when I wrote the constitution, was that the chair could only serve two years. With things that happened afterwards, I was just a foot soldier. When the Ufton Road site was turned into a playground, which Graham Parsey initiated, I was just somebody who went along and toiled. I was a local councillor by that point.

De Beauvoir was a remarkable place when we moved in. It was an artisan class place. People had these long leases, so there'd been a lot of what we now know as social cohesion. It sounds ridiculous because the gardens are quite big and there's a lot of space, but people did congregate in the early evening, in front of houses, to chat. I'm being a bit romantic about it now, but it was a very nice place. People knew each other. There were one or two middle class people who'd moved in, but mostly it was a working class area. That was 1967, '68.

The physical fabric had deteriorated. The Benyon Estate rented out some of the housing and that was in bad repair. But it didn't actually strike you – it just felt normal. I suppose you would call it planning blight but I wouldn't over-emphasise that – it's a term that belongs to the professional academic way of looking things rather than something that was felt.

...

I wanted to encourage people to strike out, so every now and then we'd organise something that everybody could do. There was a patch of land on Tottenham Road that was very dangerous, full of rubbish and spikey stuff. I said, let's go and pinch some planks of wood from this building site down the road and fence it off. Totally respectable, ordinary folk absolutely loved doing that. We had to steal the wood from the building site, but it was fun.

AND IM MUM. WORRYED OUT OF MY LIVE
IN CASE THEY GROW UP ALL DELINKWANCES.
IT WONT BE ANY FOUGHT OF MINE. I CANNOT GIVE
THEM MONEY, I CANNOT GIVE THEM A DESENT
HOME TO GROW UP
IN, I CAN ONLY
GIVE THEM MY LOVE.
THERE GETTING SO BIG
AND THE FOUR ROOM
ARE GETTING SO SMALL.
FOR THE 9 OF US.

IM
CAROL IM
SO L
BATH
OF I
UP
RO
TIM
IM
NO
A

IM
DANNY. 9
YEARS OLD,
I SLEEP
WITH TOMMY
AND TONY, IN THE
KITCHIN. AND IT ANT
HALF DAMP

IM TOMMY
IM NEALY 8.
WE HAVE GOT
RATS AND
SLUGS IN
OUR
KITCHIN
AND WE CONNOT
GO TO SLEEP TILL
GONE 12 PM.

IM.
RONNIG
IM (17)
I SLEEP
ON THE
SETTIE.
WHAT ID
GIVE TO HAVE A
BEDROOM, A
PROPER PLACE
TO SLEEP

IM TONY
IM 3.
I LIKE
WATCHING THE
MOTERS FLY ROUND
THE CORNER, WHERE
I PLAY. DANNY AND
TOMMY HAVE BEEN
RUN OVER. I SURPOSE
ILL BE NEXT AND I
LIKE, THE RATS, AND
THE SLUGS, AND
THE BEETLES.

AND I LIKE
WETING OVER
DANNY Y TOMM
IN BED

IM LORRAINE
IM 15. I SLEEP
WITH CAROL
AND SANDRA. MY
DAD SAID IF HE HURT
US HE WOULD BE SENT
TO PRISON. THE HACKNEY
HOUSEING IS NEGLECTING US
THERE MAKEING OUR LIFES
AN MISSEREY AND NOTHING
IS DONE ABOUT THEM

IM SANDRA IM
13. WE HAVE
(CAT A) OVER 5 YE
ON THE HOUSING.
THEY FEEL SORRY
THEY HAVE NOT
ENOUGH
SAID.
THEY
A BIG HOUSE
OF DOWNHAM
THATS BEEN E
SAY OUR HOME
YEARS TIME.
SAID.

ENGLAND.
THE LAND OF HOPE AND GLORY

WHAT IS HAPPYNESS

LIVEING IN THE SLUMES

AND IM DAD. I SUFFER
WITH ASMER. AND BRONCHITERS

THE SCHOOL DOCTER..

MY OWN DOCTER.

THE LONDON HOSPITAL

THE MARMAY MISSHON

. THE WELFARE

THE HEALTH DEP.

OUR. M.P.

have ALL BEEN ON TO
THE HOUSEING. NO LUCK, I COULD NOT
STAND IT, NO LONGER. I LEFT HOME.
WE ARE ALL LONDONERS, BREAD AND BORN,
IN SHOREDITCH AND HACKNEY - I SURPOZE
THERE WAITING TILL THEY ARE ALL
MARRIED OFF. WE WILL NEED A
DARBY AND JOE. HOME THEN

AN ENGLISH MANS
HOME is
HIS CASTLE
THATS
A
LaugTH

M
0
ROOM
ELIVG
LEFT
THE
SAYING
This is
t LIKE
SE

K
E
US
THERES
CORNER
OUTH GATE Rd,
3 YEARS. THEY
Down IN 3
N OUR MUM
ALL BE IN
+ HOUSE

this is not imagined this is that true and need looking into - a witness M.W.P.B.Swdf

P.S.

Things like this were pragmatic, of course, and they were born of frustration with the inability to get the council to do anything. But, for me, the prime purpose was liberation – that you don't have to rely on the bloody council. And we can have some fun. I remember when we were stealing the planks from the building site somebody said, 'What are you doing? Who gave you the authority to do this?' And I said, 'Mick'. And he said, 'There isn't a Mick on this site'.

...

The council regarded us as a total irritant. It was dominated by a very Old Left cadre of people who had been in the Young Socialists before the war – or it might have been the Young Communist League. They'd grown up together and had a very Statist approach to politics. They were very, very old-fashioned and were very strong, determined individuals: Mr and Mrs Sherman, Martin Ottolangui, a horrible little man called John Kotz and several others. They were all pretty intelligent – the Shermans had a very sophisticated grasp of what was going on in the world. Sally Sherman was my dentist for a time – a lovely woman.

We also had the most dreadful housing department, led by a man who didn't believe in tenants having any voice at all. It was an incredibly well defended organisation. When I became a councillor later, I discovered how utterly and almost deliberately inefficient the housing department was.

Because Labour was the dominant force in the borough, almost anybody would be a member of the Labour party if they were politically active, and so you genuinely had people who were essentially fascists, in the Labour party. When I became a councillor, the big thing I was on about really was the eviction policy, and the number of Labour councillors who said, they're in debt, they're rubbish, they're useless people, they deserved to be kicked out of the houses – very strong moralistic, very nasty attitude to people. They would even evict families who were fostering kids. I actually managed to turn that all round, in the end.

...

I like getting things done, I like doing things. In a way, it's the famous dictum of 'do what works'. I've always done what works in the end. Partly because, the tragedy is, there's never going to be a revolution in this country, there's never going to be a time at which everybody is a self-confident citizen able to sort out everything they need.

Obviously my class position gave me extra leverage and power, but I valued everything everybody did so it was really important that we brought everybody along. I think most of the people on the committee felt they were genuinely contributing, and they were. I had very strong relationships with a lot of the working class, or artisan class, people on the committee. In fact, they're the ones I remember best of all. In a way, the smattering of middle class people were more peripheral.

There was the imperative at the beginning of wanting to stop the council knocking the houses down. When you get an imperative like that, it gives huge impetus to whatever collective action you want to pursue. But as soon as you've won and that imperative goes, that's no longer the case. I know that the Association continues, but I'm sure it's not the same thing at all anymore.

...

Doffy, my then wife, did all the laying out of the photographs and everything like that in the *De Beaver* newsletter, and I did most of the writing. Robin may have written bits as well. But the whole purpose of it was to unify: to make sure everybody knew what was happening and would appreciate it, so it was not exactly propaganda but it was certainly very positive on the cause we were fighting.

...

People on the Left in my generation saw how the welfare state was actually working in the 1960s. We were brought up with this sense of security and that the government was beneficent and would look after people's interests, generally. But in the 1960s, organisations like Shelter and Child Poverty Action Group were beginning to say, look, we haven't abolished poverty, people are still homeless, and people are being fucked around on their benefits entitlements. You began to see the unresponsive nature of something that is such a state-driven thing. We became disillusioned, I think, and wanted to refashion the idea of welfare – not dissociating it from the state as such, but trying to reform the processes of delivery. It was never our belief that we can't afford welfare; it wasn't a turning away from the welfare state as it was – a wish that it was more responsive to people.

...

There are some other strands of activity that are quite important. One guy came to me very early on and said: 'We're trying to enfranchise our house and buy the freehold, and I've read the Leasehold Reform Act but I can't work out how it is that we're not allowed to.'

Under the Act there was a provision that the ground landlord could ensure that before people enfranchise there would be rules about how you could behave in your house, to preserve the unity of upkeep on the estate. Typical middle class kind of thing. So the Benyon Estate was using this provision to say, we're not selling to you. The idea that the estate had some kind of unity of upkeep was an obvious nonsense, because of the planning blight. A lot of leaseholders were getting quite upset and the local solicitors were on the Benyon Estate side, so they were being utterly useless.

I had a friend, a city lawyer, who was working with a group in Islington – a wonderful man called Tom Blyth. So I got Tom to be the legal representative for all 80 or 90 of the leaseholders and we called it the Leaseholders Association. We worked with Brown and Brown, the managers of the Benyon Estate. I don't think we ever had any personal contact with the Benyons, but they were basically the enemy, because they didn't develop the estate at all, they had no interest in it. Their benevolent neglect, I suppose. They were trying to stop people from buying their freeholds so obviously, so we were against them. There were two Browns: senior and junior. Brown junior was a total twot. Brown senior was a sort of 'I'm a wise person, I've seen the world' type of person, and he said to me at one stage – I can't remember which Benyon it was, the younger of the two – he said, he's a young man, very much like you. And I thought, like fuck he is!

But they were interested in the estate by the time we got organised because they were embattled. We probably succeeded in enfranchising about 60 properties. I don't think anybody in De Beauvoir Town believed in their goodwill. Well, a few did. But most people were Londoners – they were a very cynical, savvy lot of people.

We also ran a weekly Citizens Rights service and set up a tenants group to get the council to use its powers to make landlords improve their properties. It didn't work very well because the public health people in the council were not very sympathetic or helpful.

I've always believed you should give people the information they need to do things for themselves. I used to write loads of guides to social security when I was at CPAG. But I know that if I went into a social security office and said, 'this guy has nowhere to live, he needs money and it's your duty to give him money', and demanded it and put on my best Oxbridge accent, then it would happen. If he went in and did it, they'd tell him to fuck off. And they'd probably rile him until he wanted to attack them.

So there were various strands of activity going on. But this branching out, to bring in the leaseholders and the tenants, and to actually recognise there were different needs in De Beauvoir, that the Association could actually assist with, was ridiculously intensive work. But it all came about because of the DBA. There was nothing before the Association. Well, I don't know, there might have been.

...

There were some good people on the New Town Estate. But whatever success there was, it was mostly a layer, as it were, of active people, and quite a small active group on the New Town. We did come together to do certain things – I don't think there was ever a wall between us, but it was very different. The essential spirit of the DBA was that it was inclusive – that was always the idea.

I took it for granted that if people would build council housing, it ought to be fully equipped for modern life, but also that it should give people the opportunity to live in the community, and not be detached in a great fucking tower block. I did come to understand the way in which tower blocks work, in a way, afterwards, by going around the New Town. You might look at it and think, what a brutal environment, but when you went into the flats, they were all very individual and very cosy and you could tell the people there valued them, even though the actual architecture was very poor and the standards were very poor too, by then. Virtually everybody I ever met who was politically interested in De Beauvoir believed there was rampant corruption in the local authority, which actually there was.

...

There was a lot of feeling amongst the people we got involved with that the bulldozer would just sweep across De Beauvoir tranche by tranche until it reached Ball's Pond Road – that it was a remorseless process. The council just assumed it, as a matter of course. People could phone or visit them to be told when their house would be demolished. There was a sense of helplessness, I'd say.

Where the New Town Estate is, those big blocks of flats, south of Downham Road, that area had also been part of De Beauvoir Town. There'd been a public enquiry and they'd won the appeal against the council's plan to knock the houses down, but then Henry Brooke, the housing minister, ruled that the development should go ahead, and so it did. They'd fought a tremendous battle and they'd won it. And then it'd been snatched away from them.

But that isn't from personal experience, of course. I wasn't there at that time, but that was the folk memory. I don't even know if the group that fought it were simply the residents who were affected. I don't think it was a De Beauvoir-wide campaign, it was probably just those that were being attacked – they probably mobilised whatever force they could by themselves.

...

I moved to De Beauvoir because I got a job. I was a journalist, working for the *Oxford Mail*. I got really interested in social issues while I was there. I became what one person called the conscience of the *Oxford Mail*. I was writing about poverty and homelessness and so on. I got a job on *The Times* diary column so I had to find a house, and Robin was buying a house in Ball's Pond Road at that time. We were great friends, right from school onwards and the house next door was for sale as well. So, my wife and I bought the house next door to Robin.

It's curious that the lasting legacy of the DBA is that it physically survived, and within it, there is some social housing because Robin bought about 60 houses as the De Beauvoir Trust. We worked on *The Times* diary column together and there was a filing cabinet in our room that was all Trust business. He was absolutely brilliant.

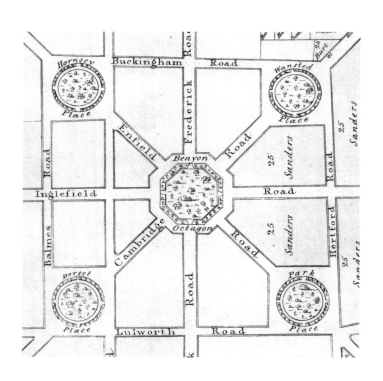

Plan for Beauvoir Town Estate. 1821

EDWARD BENYON

The De Beauvoir family and the Benyon family met in India. The first Richard Benyon was an orphan, brought up by his godfather. He was sent to India at the age of thirteen, with a one-way ticket, to work for the East India Company. He was obviously a very bright boy because he worked his way up to being governor of what was then Fort St George which became Madras – and is now Chennai. He came back in the early 1700s with a fortune and bought an estate in Essex, near Downham, close to his friend Osmond de Beauvoir. De Beauvoir was the husband of the daughter of the Governor of Bengal, and the inheritor of, among other things, the Hackney estate his father had bought a generation before.

Osmond de Beauvoir had a niece called Mary Tyson, who had married the heir to Englefield House and Estate in Berkshire. He died and so Mary Tyson was left with this huge house and fortune. As the story goes – though it's probably not true – Osmond de Beauvoir was worried she might then do something silly like marry a Catholic, so he introduced her to Richard Benyon, and the two fell in love and married. Benyon later acquired other estates in Essex such as Culford Hall and Downham. So he and his wife Mary Tyson now owned several estates.

Osmond's son Peter de Beauvoir was heir to the Hackney estate and the rest of the De Beauvoir land. He lived to 88 and he was a miserly old bachelor. He left his fortune to his next-of-kin, who was my great great great great uncle, and grandson of Mary Tyson and Richard Benyon, and also called Richard.

Interestingly, quite a few people had to die in order for my great uncle to be next-of-kin to Peter de Beauvoir at the time of his death. If Peter hadn't lived until 88, it might have been someone else. Equally, Richard had two younger brothers who were both killed in the Napoleonic wars, whom Peter de Beauvoir preferred, and so they might well have got it instead. Either way, it all would have been very different. The fact that it came down as it did is truly remarkable.

Peter de Beauvoir had signed a building lease with William Rhodes just before his death in 1821. William Rhodes was quite an impressive guy, a big farmer. He'd got a building lease on this Hackney estate; he took a lot of clay out, which he used to make bricks to make the basin and some stuff on Stamford Road and elsewhere. He hadn't done much more than that when Richard Benyon inherited the estate and after a couple of years challenged Rhodes' lease. The case went all the way to the House of Lords. Benyon won but had to pay Rhodes' costs which came to 20 grand, which in those days was a huge amount of money!

So, Richard Benyon then sold off land under building leases to build De Beauvoir Town, to a different plan to the one Rhodes had commissioned. Leases were sold off to builders, who had to build in an agreed style, and then the builders, in turn, would sell off 50-year leases to the people moving in. But Richard had a very strong connection to the area. He was passionate about it, and how it was going to end up. He built the church – he built seven churches, in fact, including the one here.

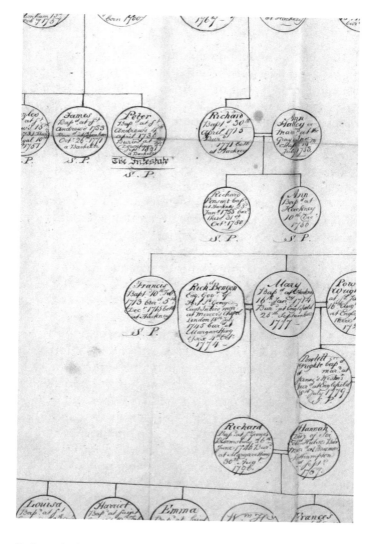

Pedigree in the case of De Beauvoir vs Benyon. c.1821 – c.1864

...

Today, we have just under 400 leases of different shapes and form, in about 220 properties, but everything on a map of De Beauvoir Town belonged to us at some point. Every property will have our name on the deeds. The compulsory purchased properties – which includes everything south of Downham Road, of course – won't, because the title is wiped clean by this process, but everywhere else, you'll see us on the title at some point.

It wouldn't be good for De Beauvoir if we owned the whole thing today. Some of our newer tenants are families and stay for a long time, but most of them are young, transient sharers, who probably don't necessarily contribute to the local community as much as owner occupiers. We still have 72 protected tenants which date back to before Thatcher's changes in 1989 and their homes for life.

Governments should look at this security business. People should be allowed to rent a house for ten years, to educate a child in the same primary and secondary school. One of the things that makes De Beauvoir so dynamic is the cross-section of people you get here. I'm looking at how we can introduce more affordable housing and how the private sector can create affordable housing. Ten per cent of our tenancies are at affordable rents. We do that partly by lowering the spec, so they're not done to the tip-top spec that people pay the maximum rent for. On top of that, my father set up our own charitable foundation which we use to support local initiatives – in a small way, not in a big way. Down at

Englefield, nearby there's an old Elizabethan manor owned by the estate. That is now an educational trust, run by my sister. We're a business foremost; I have a job and I report to a board – some of it is family but a lot are not family. I have to produce figures that show that we are operating in a business-like fashion but we have to do this within our social conscience.

...

I started to come here around 1970, when I was eight and my parents moved into Northchurch Terrace. I remember my mother being very excited about the road closures – the initial road closures that went in temporarily in the early 1970s. It really changed the area because it was a rat run before then. But this crossroads here – between Culford, Lawford and Northchurch – my mother remembers a chap who used to come and lunge his horse in the middle of that.

...

It was quite an affluent area when it was built, but it declined in the early part of the 20th century. It bottomed-out around the Second World War and then it started coming up again through the 1970s and 1980s, but it didn't really start to fly until the 1990s.

So during the 1940s and 1950s – and I think probably also in the 1930s – the area was pretty run-down and obviously, that was the council's argument at that time for knocking it all down. You couldn't get a building license to build a garden shed then, because there were no raw materials. The rents were so low, it was always a question for us of how to get the money together to bring the houses up to scratch. None of them had inside bathrooms – everyone used the local bathhouse. So in the 1960s we sold off some long leases so that we could move people out of really run-down property and do it up, to prove to the council that these properties were worth keeping and they could be restored.

My father's predecessor was Harry Benyon. He had no children, so when he died in 1959 the estate was left to his cousin, my grandfather. My family all changed our name in 1964 – I was born Shelley – and moved into Englefield House, which my brother still lives in.

When Harry Benyon died, death duties were then 80 per cent of the whole of the family holdings. I'm still not quite sure why we're still here today – very wise and careful stewardship of my father and grandfather, basically. A number of properties had to be sold off, and then in 1967 the first Leasehold Reform Act allowed leaseholders to buy their freehold. Two-thirds of our properties in De Beauvoir were eligible. That was a major blow, because we'd been selling leases to pay for the buildings to be renovated. And many other properties were still under lease from decades before. The first leases sold in the mid-1800s were for 50 years, so they came up again in 1900 and many were sold for 70 years, which was quite normal in those days. That took them past 1967, so in all, the Leasehold Reform Act meant we were forced to sell hundreds of houses.

So there are three main reasons the Benyon Estate is no longer the size it once was: death duties, leasehold reform and compulsory purchase. There are other things, as well – the Luftwaffe had a bit of a go.

In the early 1970s we sold a lot of leases with set ground rents so they wouldn't fall foul of the 1967 Act, but the ground rent would still be reviewed every 25 years. So each time that comes around, you look at the plot that the house sits on, imagine there is no house on it, and calculate the ground rent from that. But of course, by the 1990s, land values were rising sharply, so people suddenly found their ground rent going from a few hundred to a few thousand pounds a year. The Estate was then managed remotely by a firm of surveyors so our interests weren't reported first hand. This made us very unpopular. It was a very bad time for my father because he wasn't actively involved but he was the head of it and he got all the flack. I've got a copy of the letter that Margaret Thatcher wrote to him, saying 'what on earth are you doing?'. People had written to her. I've got all the old press cuttings, and it's not happy reading.

I think there are an awful lot of solicitors out there that didn't advise people of the consequences. If you buy a lease with a ground rent review in 25 years' time, you don't even think about it, do you? And leasehold was much more normal then than it is now. In those days it was used by this sort of urban estate as a method of raising money to spend on the rest of the estate without letting go of the ownership of the property.

TRUST

Already converted

108, De Beauvoir Road

7, Culford Grove,

113, Tottenham Road.

Work proceeding in:

52, Mortimer Road *occup~*

12, Ardleigh Road *work in progress*

105, Tottenham Road *work in progress*

123, Tottenham Road *Occupied*

125, Culford Road *work in progress*

30, Englefield Road *Work in progress*

Now ~~sxxd~~ owned by Trust:

39, Ardleigh Road, *• Crack*

149, Culford Road, *Await Council decase.*

98, Mortimer Road *• Tender*

60, Culford Road *Refused Ply Perm to convert due to southern Ath consolidate. one owner yean*

139, Balls Pond Road *Grave for GLC work in prog*

Contracts exchanged for:

37a, Stamford Road, *• Work in progress*

29, De Beauvoir Square, *Tenders*

44, Englefield Road *Tenant in exist to be decanted into 125 Culford*

?44 *Uftn ?Bcvrs LH selly rehoused by Council*

Lott 5 in SA due to military thirders available on 10tm of Trust Securty put

Terms agreed for:

7, Buckingham Road, *Await decaiy*

427, Kingsland Road, *• Work in progress*

109, De Beauvoir Road, *Tenders/decased*

70, De Beauvoir Road,

Negotiations proceeding:

58, Culford Road, ✓

78, Culford Road, ✓

71, Mortimer Road, *owned by Trust.*

133, Culford Road, ✓

4.

and various cottages in Tottenham Rd.

148, 152, Scott Ford

The Trust has now also written off for recognition by Clacton UDC with the possibility of providing some seaside retirement homes too!

Both Represented bought up & owners of Breades

R.

240

We had already started the De Beauvoir Association to try and protect the local environment and the local community. We thought, if we're successful in stopping that council from demolishing the whole of De Beauvoir Town, as they had south of Downham Road, we ought to do something to ensure there's some affordable housing available in the area.

It was very lucky, but 1968 had seen the election, rather to their own surprise, of a Conservative administration in Hackney, which was entirely unheard of. They went from having no representatives to having control of the council. They were so green and uninformed that they had to draft in six Aldermen with a bit of experience and nous to provide themselves with some policies. We provided them, in effect, with a policy, because a housing association wasn't council development but it was similar and it was providing social housing, so they could get hold of that and run with it, so to speak.

As far as I know, they weren't keen to develop the north of De Beauvoir but the plans were still there and the officers, possibly, were still harbouring their scheme. The De Beauvoir Trust gave the Conservatives an excuse to wipe their hands of it.

...

Stuart and I are rather a funny pair, really, because we were at school together, we were at college together, and when I bought my house on Ball's Pond Road, the one next-door was for sale as well, and

Stuart bought that. So, we were quite an effective partnership.

We both worked for *The Times*. Stuart was influential in getting me appointed a year after we'd both applied for the same vacancy – he got the first one and I got the next one, thanks to Stuart, largely. The diary, at that time – it seems ridiculous now – they had a staff of five, and I think there was actually an intention to appoint a sixth. But that left us all a bunch of spare time – anybody could run a housing association in the spare time I had!

The diary editor was the one who was most likely to object, but he didn't. Stuart was running the Citizens Rights office out of his filing cabinet. So he had a hobby on the side as well. Inevitably, if you're a journalist, you ring people up and they're not there, so you ask them to ring back, and that leaves you some time to make a call to an estate agent to say 'got anything for sale?'.

...

I wasn't aware of any other similar group. The other housing associations operating nearby were professionally staffed, and De Beauvoir was just a little island of this rather anomalous self-service community action group.

The first house that we converted was, I think, 108 De Beauvoir Road. We had the Minister of Housing from the government come down to open it and bask in the reflected glory of this new start. At the same time we converted, I think it was, number 2 Culford Road. Thereafter, I just went after everything that came up for sale in De Beauvoir Town, whether it was tenanted or vacant possession.

The majority of our houses were three-storey – you know, the classic De Beauvoir – which gave you a maisonette upstairs and a basement flat downstairs. I don't think we ever acquired anything that was overcrowded. Mostly it was a question of people dying. The tenanted properties that we bought, the gentrifiers weren't much interested in, because they didn't want to be bothered with tenants. There would have been some pressure from landlords trying to get people out in order to cash in on the value of the vacant freehold and De Beauvoir Association would have been active in opposing that and backing the tenants and trying to keep them in place.

It was a time of really rapidly changing house prices and not all the estate agents were as alive to the dynamic of the situation as others. We were able to get quite fantastic bargains on some houses. The cheapest was a fire-damaged property in Culford Road which we bought for £750, which was a fantastically low price. It made very little difference to us that it was fire-damaged because we would have been stripping it and gutting it and redoing the interior from new anyway.

Oakley Brown were the estate agents for the Benyon Estate, and they were the sleepiest about. They had very little idea of what the value of things were and I did get several properties off them. They were very old-fashioned. Their office was more like a rent collection centre than an estate agents' office – they didn't have any window display or 'properties for sale' or anything alarmingly modern like that!

...

I was called the Secretary of the De Beauvoir Trust.
I had a committee – they were mostly De Beauvoir
Association people. But I made it a condition –
and this is being very frank – that I couldn't be the
Secretary and, in effect, the developing agent, if I
was to be having to bother about having committee
meetings all the time about everything, so the
committee hardly ever met – or, quite baldly, never
met – and I just told them what I was doing and they
had to go along with it.

Really we continued as what you might call a
benevolent autocracy, until the time came when
I really couldn't continue to run it as a volunteer
in my spare time without any reward, or office, or
facilities at all. I ran it, in effect, out of a drawer in
Lord Thomson's *Times* building. All the phone calls
were made at Lord Thomson's expense; all the letters
were paid for by Lord Thomson's postage. It got to
the stage where I couldn't really pretend to be up
to the administration of what was becoming quite a
big operation. I think, from memory, we had 52 units
converted and occupied by the time we merged with
Circle 33, and about 50 houses that we'd purchased,
so it was quite a big operation for any one person to
be running.

Stuart Weir insisted that we couldn't just merge
with Circle 33 over the tenants' heads – we had to
consult them and get their approval. I thought this
was pretty ridiculous, because we couldn't present
them with any real choice. It did go forward with
the approval of the tenants. Their opportunity

to disapprove was there, but it was a pretty slim opportunity, really, because there was only one housing association that was interested in merging with us. The others thought that De Beauvoir was too up-and-coming to be an area in which they could afford housing. That was ridiculous because I'd already bought 50 bloomin' houses, and that proved you could do it if you tried.

...

I became a trustee of Circle 33 so that I could continue to look after the interests of the De Beauvoir Trust – or De Beauvoir tenants – from their committee. And I continued until 1978, I think.

Circle 33 was entirely different because it was a fully staffed, professional organisation. Even so, their rate of acquisition in De Beauvoir was rather lower than what I had been achieving as a sole operator but then, I was on the ground and I rang the estate agents every week to find out if anything new was coming onto the market so that I could start getting estimates and designs done by the surveyor and architect we had as collaborators. They were, of course, professionals, but their reward came out of the costs of the conversion; they were, in effect, paid by the GLC through De Beauvoir Trust.

I didn't have to raise any money, except from the GLC. You had to show them that you were acquiring the property at an affordable price and that your conversion would come in within costs, so that at the rent charged, you would be covering the expense of what, in effect, was a mortgage. We didn't operate very much through the local council, largely because their officers were very slow to react – I needed to get a fairly rapid response as to whether councils were willing to provide the money to buy houses and convert them, and the Greater London Council was a lot more efficient.

It was a steep learning curve. I had some help from a man who was with the Notting Hill housing association. He explained the broad principles of it to me, but after that I just went in the deep end and started applying to the GLC, getting forms and filling them out and banging them back!

...

I saw it as a means of giving working people a chance to live in the area still, through providing social housing to the best of our ability. One of the ironic things about this was that we were, in effect, through the housing association, trying to counter the gentrification of De Beauvoir but we were ourselves part of that gentrification.

In one public meeting, I was asked how big I would like De Beauvoir Trust to become and I said, ideally I would like De Beauvoir Trust to be able to buy every property that's for sale in De Beauvoir Town. That was seized upon by a thing called the Hackney Gutter Press – me as the wicked landlord wanting to put tenants on the rack. That was the heading on their article, and I was painted as a very bad influence.

...

One condition of operating with the GLC was that the GLC provided us with nominations for tenancies. From memory I think I was able to put forward nominees myself, and of course we took responsibility for tenants who were already in the houses that we bought: if we bought a tenanted property, we were obliged to rehouse the tenants. So that chimed with our intention of keeping the community together. The GLC nominations weren't necessarily from outside the area either; for instance, one of the earliest people we rehoused was a teacher in the De Beauvoir primary school who until then was commuting from somewhere in Lambeth, I think. Because she was a local teacher, and had applied to us, we were able to rehouse her.

I suppose it's fair to say we did part from that policy of local rehousing to some degree, because we took three nominations for Ugandan Asians. You'll remember that at that time Idi Amin was kicking all the Asians out and there was a general need – much like the migrants' situation now, on a much smaller scale. I did consult the committee about this, but we decided that it was a good idea and I rehoused three families.

...

The De Beauvoir Association operated as a sort of open meeting and anybody who lived in the area could come to the meetings, so there wasn't a committee as such. The committee was whoever turned up. And there were people who turned up who'd lived in the area all their lives. They were very keen and enthusiastic. They'd simply lacked any leadership before. Before we arrived, there just hadn't been anybody to say, come on, we can do something about this, let's set to and organise something.

We produced a newsletter called *De Beaver* – because that's how a lot of people pronounced it locally – so *De Beaver* became a newsletter distributed to all the houses, and that brought in people who had been in the community a long time but hadn't actually had a community organisation to identify with before.

Stuart was very good because, for instance, on that opening of our first house, Stuart managed to wangle sponsorship by Ideal Standard, the sanitary ware firm, so that we got free bogs and hand basins and baths for it in return for acknowledging their help when the government minister came to open it. Nobody else would have the nous or the application to do that.

...

The basic thing was, we don't want this area redeveloped in the way that the council are proposing. I think that what they had in mind for north of De Beauvoir was more like south of Downham Road. If we didn't want it redeveloped, then we had to do something else.

Any campaigning that there had been against the demolition south of Downham Road had obviously been unsuccessful. That was all over and done with by the time Stuart and I arrived on the scene. I wasn't aware of any campaigning that there had been, in fact.

We had one set of squatters. They moved into a house in, I think, Culford Road. It was finished and was on the point of being reoccupied when we found the squatters were in it. I remember they painted one of the internal walls black.

At that time, you had to get the names of the squatters to get a court order against them to get them out. So I went down in my role as *Times* journalist, to interview them about their presence in this property. I didn't tell them I was the secretary of the housing association that they were victimising, but I got the interviews about why they were squatting and what their attitudes to councils and renting generally was. And I got their names, and then took out court orders against them. Of course, they eventually moved out the day before the court hearing was due.

I think they were people who'd just got fed up with being on the housing list, with no particular hope of being rehoused. A phrase that I remember was a woman saying she was 'going to go down the town hall with a bloody axe'.

The Playground needs YOUR Support NOW !

Does your child go to the playground?
Do you know other children who use the playground?
Are you interested in the playground?

Yes? Then you will know how important it is that the
playground stays open. You may not think so, but it
takes time and money to run it!

If we can't raise more money the playground will have
to close by the end of the summer.

With just a little of your time the playground can be
a better and more exciting place.

so please come to the playground
SUNDAY MAY 18th   3·30

- coffee and tea
- mini jumble sale by the kids
- childrens' painting

- meet the kids and the playleaders
- see the site
- give us your ideas!
- let's make this a regular event

Support Your Playground - Dont let it Close

ALAN RAYNER

We were doing various community activist-type things in the 1970s. I was involved with the surveys – I went round and knocked on people's doors and asked them whether I could check out what sort of loos they've got and that sort of thing, and see what their complaints were. There were still a large number of places with deficient bathrooms, outside loos and all that sort of thing, and not all tenanted – some were owner-occupied.

There was a big question of managing expectations because if people have somebody coming around asking those sorts of questions, they imagine that something might happen, whereas, in effect, it didn't, because all we could do was produce some statistics to the council and say, we've done the survey, there's X percent who've got this feature and Y percent have got something else. But the council were genuinely concerned to get an improvement in the quality of the places, the quality of life. There wasn't the motivation of saying, we've got to do down the council. The objective was to say to the council: let's all be on the same side; we have identified a problem, now you as professionals can follow through on that. Occasionally one does have to operate in a party political sense, by fighting elections and such like. But then I've never won any election, not since I was at university. I only won then because what I said was so outrageous that people said, 'oh, we'll give this guy a chance'.

...

The Labour party was the only show in town, so to speak, in the early days. They had always felt entitled to rule. There was a minority of people – including Stuart Weir – that wanted change and had a more 'community involvement' approach but certainly not as strong as it was later, when it became one of the trademarks of the Liberals. Even at that time with the local Liberal party, the idea was to get under the party organisations to get to people, and to get people to take responsibility for their own lives.

My involvement with party politics has always been subservient to my basic ideas of people getting involved. When people ask me, I say that one of my generating principles is informed consent. I'm keen that people should be informed about what the possibilities are, and that they should consent on the basis of proper information about them. The difficulty is getting people to accept that approach.

...

What triggered the reaction in the community was the demolition plans, and from both sides of the argument. There were people coming along to the meetings who wanted the demolition plans to go ahead so they could get re-housed and others who saw it being a waste of resources.

The initial meetings that were set up eventually led to the establishment of the DBA. Those meetings provided people with an opportunity to see that they could do something differently. They had an innate sense that something is going to change. They didn't know in what way but they just felt that 'this is something that I need to get involved with and find out what's going on'.

I suspect that if there hadn't been that catalyst provided by the initial DBA group, there wouldn't have been any major revolt later on. People would have just accepted it and they would have either been re-housed or not, as the case may be. People get fed up with bashing their heads against the wall. They will wait on the waiting list for housing for 15 or 20 years. Others will say, 'you should go round there and demand this, that and the other' but the response would be, 'I've done that in the past, and it doesn't get anywhere'.

...

The approach in the Labour party at the time was to demolish everything, rebuild and start again. I suspect it may well have been developed in the 1950s, when there was an emphasis on building 300,000 houses a year – and from a Conservative government. And they were all council houses.

The Conservative-controlled council from 1968 really took up the General Improvement Area issue. To an extent they were playing party politics but I think there was a genuine concern about conserving resources, which is, of course, what Conservatives are about.

I probably looked at it in terms of resources. If you knock down a property and you rebuild it, then that is going to cost more than doing a reasonable refurbishment job. People could see that the old property had some value and there was some sort of beauty in it. I don't know when it came into place, but there was a movement towards that view.

...

We always had access to the Ufton Centre building since it had been abandoned by the Women's Royal Voluntary Service. They left a load of things in there. We found a huge tub of old hotel soaps – I had a supply for years. We found some old prams, so we had a pram race one time.

We had meetings to discuss things like floor coverings and uses of spaces, internal stud partitions, heating and all that sort of thing, but I don't remember any of the details. It was like any community organisation: there are the key people who had a gradual change-over and then there's the next surrounding group of people who are generally 'in the know' but aren't necessarily right at the centre of things. There would be a gradual drifting between those two groups and then the outer group will have a drifting off outside. Occasionally we would lose somebody from the inner group because they would move away or have a different lifestyle or whatever. So that's why there needs to be this outer group of people who are, what one might call, attenders, who come in and see what's involved.

To a certain extent my whole life has been about voluntary activity because I've taken the view that if I've got an adequate income, then everything else I do is free of charge. Sometimes I would be down at the Hunger Project in west London until three o'clock in the morning, and then I'd get in and do my day-

remains, why?'

.why build an estate for a 1000 households & only provide a handful of swings for recreation?'

Play Association who will speak on how another community has sought answers to similar questions.
ie. GOLBORNE, Nth KENSINGTON etc

used for recreational use? Meeting organised by the DE BEAUVOIR ASSOCIATION you don't have to be a member to attend!

.next year the central GIA proposals may be implemented why not use some of the vacant sites NOW to gain valuable experience on short term facilities?'

.last year the cottages in Enfield Rd. were cleared for the expansion of the school which this year we hear may be closed altogether. What will become of the site?'

.why can't the canal be used for recreational use? Meeting organised by the DE BEAUVOIR ASSOCIATION you don't have to be a member to attend!

an invitation to you all!
DE BEAUVOIR PLAYTHING
THIS WED 8th / 8.45

in the CRYPT: ST. PETER'S CHURCH
Northchurch Road. N1.

SOMEWHERE to PLAY

a 25 minute film followed by
PAT SMYTHE

Organiser: Kensington & Chelsea Play Association who will speak on how another community has sought answers to similar questions.
ie. GOLBORNE, Nth KENSINGTON etc

IF YOU OR YOUR CHILDREN ASK THESE QUESTIONS, THIS MEETING CONCERNS YOU!

.how long must the vacant prefab sites remain derelict, dangerous & unfenced; and how can the community benefit from them?'

.the community centre site in Downham Rd. has remained derelict for 2 summers whilst the desperate need for playspace in the New Town and southern area remains, why?'

.why build an estate for a 1000 households & only provide a handful of swings for recreation?'

.next year the central GIA proposals may be implemented why not use some of the vacant sites NOW to gain valuable experience on

an invitation to you all!
DE BEAUVOIR PLAYTHING

IF YOU OR YOUR CHILDREN ASK THESE QUESTIONS, THIS MEETING CONCERNS YOU!

.how long must the vacant prefab sites remain derel-

work at ten o'clock in the morning. But it was only every other day.

...

The Tai Chi at the Ufton Centre was the cheapest in London because we got support from the Inner London Education Authority. We had people from all over northeast London. And we had a few community dances – I remember one in particular where we all felt really good at the end of the evening because we'd come together for some jiving about, or whatever.

The northern-most bay of the Centre became a youth centre, and we had a small office for a youth leader who was able to run projects from there. For a couple of summers project workers would be recruited from local people but then it became formalised and there wasn't any need for me to be there. I think I was on at least one interview panel – there was a guy who came up from St Lucia through the Community Service Volunteers one summer, living in one of the De Beauvoir Trust properties in Stamford Road.

I was also involved with the Inner City Theatre Company, later on – it was set up in 1982, with funding from the Greater London Council and government schemes, because we provided employment for actors. The idea was that those who were officers of the DBA should take on a liaison role with organisations using the Ufton Centre. I got saddled with the Inner City Theatre Company, which took the southern-most bay of the building. We used the bay as a rehearsal space, a scenery-building space and such like, and then the company would go on tour. A lot of the scripts came from the space of encouraging people to be aware that there was a different way of approaching society and it wasn't all about making money for vast corporations and that sort of thing.

The people involved in the Ufton Centre were locals and we had a sense of ownership. But we didn't dig into our own pockets to any great extent, so we were dependent upon getting funding from elsewhere. Our contribution was our time.

Somebody would come up with an idea, and in most cases it would have been accepted. We had the space, but obviously there were logistical things like making sure there was a time slot in which it could happen, sorting out who had the keys, those sorts of things. But largely if somebody had a good idea, then it would happen.

It was in the spirit of using what was already there and making use of those resources. Plus the ethos of people like Graham Parsey and a number of other people in the area, who felt there was a need to get the community involved. And to give expression for, for want of a better term, this De Beauvoir-ishness. I know it's not a good term but it sums up the separation of De Beauvoir and having a distinctive area, which people had a real association with, separate to anywhere. De Beauvoir always had a sense of being 'semi-detached' from the rest of Hackney – but never aligned with Islington.

Graham's concern was for getting the community to take responsibility and get involved. And that was more my side of it. I saw the political side of it not as a major objective, but in support of the community side. I was more motivated by the community and expressing that through politics rather than the other way round, like Stuart Weir, who was interested in the politics and expressing it through the community.

...

What eventually led to the demise of the Ufton Centre, I think, was the lack of people with the personal commitment to keep things going, rather than the funding, necessarily. The dynamism came from the people and a lot of those who had been involved weren't participating in the same way, myself included. Although I was living opposite the Centre and I still was involved there, I can't remember any major initiatives from the late 1980s.

The whole ethos had been voluntary – people contributing what they could and what they felt comfortable with doing. We muddled along on that basis until we found that suddenly we couldn't do as much as we had done in the past, and things dropped by the wayside and faded. I think that's probably the way a lot of voluntary groups operate.

With the DBA and the Ufton Centre we got to the stage where there were more requirements to interact with the local authorities. There's much more commissioning that goes on now. And this means that people are saying, 'well I'm just involved with red tape now', and things are no longer the dynamic ventures of the 1970s, like the Ufton Centre and the DBA.

There was this sense of empowerment in the area in the 1970s, a sense that people could make a change. In the 1980s that wore off a little bit. By the 1980s we said, 'well, we've been doing all this for 10 years. Maybe we should consider, is it of any great value to us and to the community?' Certainly, I felt by the mid-1980s that I no longer had the enthusiasm, the inspiration for doing these things in the way I had done previously.

...

I'd always wanted to go back to El Hierro. The first time I went there was in 1989. There's an island off Devon called Lundy which I've been visiting since 1962 and so this idea of an off-shore island has always been something which intrigued me. I'd been going back there fairly often until 2004, and now I live there.

I have been promoting El Hierro and its pioneering renewable electricity generating scheme. What they do is pump water to a huge reservoir high up a mountain, about 700 metres, under wind power. And then when they want to have their electricity, they let water out from the top reservoir, so it flows down to the bottom, operating hydroelectric turbines, which generate electricity.

The water can be pumped up there any time the wind blows, and then they can draw electricity whenever they want, just by letting out some water, which goes down to the lower reservoir where it can come back up again when the wind blows. And it's very windy at the moment. Some people are saying it can be used as a model for other places.

UPTON PLAYSCHEME 1981

	JULY 27th	AUGUST 3rd	AUGUST 10th	AUGUST 17th	AUGUST 24th	AUGUST 31st
MONDAY	SWIMMING (LUTON RD BATHS) 2–3pm — 27th	CLIMBING FRAME — Theatre — 3rd	CLIMBING FRAME — 10th	BADGE MACHINE (HPA) — 17th	— 24th	— 31st
TUESDAY	LITTLEHAMPTON (COACH) — 28th	CLIMBING FRAME — 4th	SWIMMING (LUTON RD BATHS) 2–5pm — 11th	— 18th	SWIMMING (LUTON ROAD BATH) 2–5pm — 25th	2-4-6-8 HACKNEY PLAYBUS – PUPPETS — SEPT 1st
WEDNESDAY	— 29th	SWIMMING (LUTON ROAD BATHS) 2–5pm — 5th	LUTON ABBEY (COACH) — 12th	LAZERDOWN (COACH) — 19th	STEEPLADES (COACH) — 26th	SWIMMING (LUTON ROAD BATHS) 2–5pm — 2nd
THURSDAY	10–12.30 HACKNEY PLAYBUS – C. CRAFTS — 30th	HACKNEY LIBRARY BOOK BUS 10.30–12.30 — 6th	— 13th	10–12.30 HACKNEY PLAYBUS – POTTERY — 20th	ALL DAY – EXPERIENCE TOBOGGAN (DENIM CARPET SHOES) — 27th	SOUTHEND (COACH) — 3rd
FRIDAY	MINIBUS (HPA) — 31st	(HPA) — 7th	MINIBUS (HPA) — 14th	MINIBUS (HPA) — 21st	MINIBUS (HPA) S.N.C.A. Sally & me — 28th	S.N.C.A. — 4th

Large spanning letters across the AUGUST 17th / AUGUST 24th columns: P → ... A ... M ... C ← ; also "(HPA) S.N.C.A."

CAROL LEE

At some time in the late 1970s a committee must have been formed to decide what should happen to the derelict factory on Ufton Road – a mix of local people and representatives from the council. Fairly late on, I was asked to join in by a neighbour of mine. At that time I don't think much was happening on the site; there was a skateboarding area, but that was about it.

In 1978 and '79 the two factory buildings started to be done up with a government trainee scheme for the building trades. I must admit, when I moved into my house in 1977 the garden was a wilderness of blackberry bushes, corrugated iron, lumps of wood and general detritis, so I threw much of it over the back wall into the factory site. I had a ladder propped up against the back wall to help my efforts for weeks.

...

The southern building was designated a community centre and the northern building a youth club. It was decided that the opening night should be a Victorian evening, held in the youth club. I went to that and did an awful lot of washing up, I suppose because I was on the committee. I made myself a long black velvet skirt with a red frilly petticoat underneath and a white Laura Ashley blouse with tight cuffs and flouncing down the front. I think there was a lace insertion and I had a boater with roses in it. Sadly no photos as I was really hard up then and didn't have a camera.

I think there was beer at the opening event and even some idea of having a licence to have alcohol at events in the community centre. It must have been hashed over in a committee meeting but it didn't go ahead because we couldn't sell enough barrels to make it workable. I don't think the community centre ever really got off the ground. There was a lunch club for elderly people and I think there was a nursery but not much else happened, to my memory at least. Someone was appointed to organise it but perhaps he wasn't dynamic enough to really get it going.

In 1981 there was an Easter holiday playscheme and another one in the summer, both of which I also helped at. I think I got paid a bit – not a lot. Some people from the estate were helpers in the holiday scheme and most of the children who came were from there. I'm not sure they were terribly well run because people weren't very experienced in doing it. But a lot of mothers were working and it was a place where children could go, so it was a great help to them that there were adults keeping an eye on them.

At one stage the youth club was really successful and run by a good leader called Jim. My sons enjoyed going but when he left it sadly went downhill. The club was broken into several times and stuff was stolen, then it caught fire – maybe more than once. I suppose there wasn't really anyone keeping a close eye on it and the whole scheme just fizzled out.

From about 1985/6 the factory was left abandoned but in 1993 a planning application was put in to build new houses and flats on the site, with a big courtyard in the middle. Those of us living close by thought too many homes had been proposed. There was quite a movement to reduce the numbers, led by Ian

Palmer from Ufton Road and I think, as a result, the development was scaled down a little.

...

Many of the houses on my road originally belonged to the Benyon Estate. By the time I came, my house and the next few belonged to the council. They did mine up in 1977, just before I moved in. My neighbour said it had been empty and derelict for seven years. It was probably built in the 1850s. It's got two skins of bricks and in between there is just rubble. And as for foundations, I don't think there are any. Originally the southern end of the street began further south, near the canal, but that was flattened in the 1960s for the De Beauvoir Estate flats – hence the first house in the road now is number 39.

Before I came here, my three young children and I were in a block of flats close to Old Street, as council tenants. We were on the 13th floor so I applied to move and, in fact, my house was the fourth offer I so luckily received. The other three were quite unsuitable so when I got the fourth my father brought us round to have a look. The downstairs windows were covered in corrugated iron but I managed to peer through the letterbox and saw a radiator, so that was that – success. I later exercised my Right to Buy. What a stroke of luck to live in an area that has become so gentrified!

...

When I first came here, there was an elderly lady called Joyce living a few doors down who could remember horses with black plumes pulling coffin carriages from the yard at the end of the road. I always think of it as Brundles' yard because they were there for years, making nails and wire netting. No doubt they were offered a goodly sum by developers, because it's now a gated development. Next door was Mr. Emanuel, who ran a small printing business, in what one might call a back building.

I've lived in De Beauvoir for almost 40 years now, which seems unbelievable. I still have a clear memory of our first night in my house and turning the light on. When another light was turned on the light reduced by half and a third meant we were in twilight – thanks, Hackney Council. I hope I've been fairly civic in my time here. I've been involved in the Ufton Factory committee, the De Beauvoir Gardening Club, the De Beauvoir Association, the National Gardens Scheme and the Conservation Area Advisory Committee, looking at local planning applications. In all of those things, I suppose we have wanted to do things for other people, but not necessarily what other people have always wanted! Though I've made some wonderful friends from being involved in such things. My neighbour for many years was a born and bred Hackneyite. She persuaded me to go with her to a ladies' night at the Mitre pub on the south side of Downham Road on one occasion. There was a stripper who pranced about amidst the throng showing absolutely nothing interesting and gay men dressed up in beautiful gowns who sang, I think. The place was absolutely heaving.

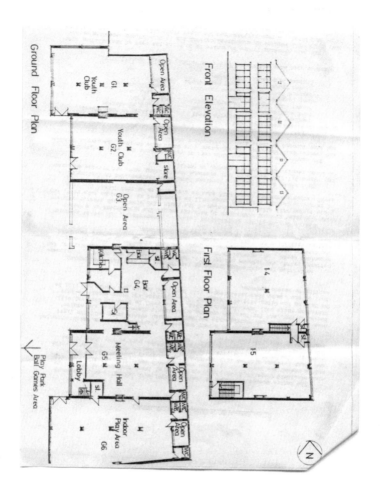

Plan of Ufton Centre former factory buildings. 1981

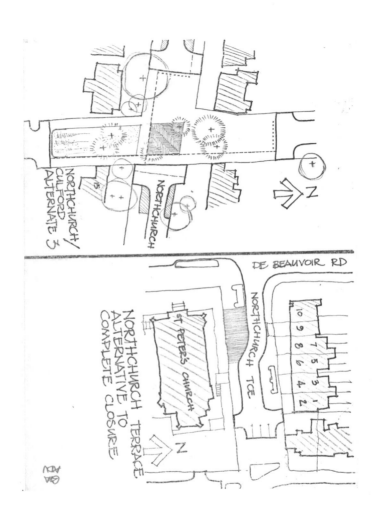

Sketch by Graham Parsey. Date unknown

HAYDEN PARSEY

It seems incredible when I look at De Beauvoir today. This beautiful area close to the City of London, with its quiet, wide streets and generously proportioned houses, is the epitome of gentrified splendour. Yet just over 40 years ago, it was held in such low regard by Hackney Council that it was to be demolished in its entirety. The council letters had been dispatched and dates set for people to vacate their homes so that, street by street, they could be demolished in 'six months from the above date' to create council estates over the entire area.

A few of its best inhabitants fought for their lives to prevent this from happening and my father Graham Parsey was one of them. He chaired the De Beauvoir Association, started the *De Beaver* newspaper, which he wrote and edited, ensured that the neighbourhood got conservation area status and successfully campaigned for the council to completely reverse their position. Once secured, he then continued by seizing land on Ufton Road to create a community centre and a playspace which still exists today, designing the cycle routes and road closure system that is so admired for filtering the traffic and drew up plans for street architecture that was implemented in full. Later on, he chaired the Conservation Area Advisory Committee, so his involvement was considerable and ongoing.

Initially, Graham was probably the greatest pain in the backside Hackney Council had ever encountered. But over time he was basically writing council policy through his recommendations and steering committee. Hackney did not have an official planning policy, it was so bamboozled. Graham presented them with expert solutions and they would implement them, unofficially of course, as though they were their own bright ideas. Latterly he would have been consulted informally on many new developments in the borough. He was formidable and relentless and the De Beauvoir that exists today, perhaps even the Hackney that exists today, is very much the result of his vision. When I look back over the achievements of his life, and there were many, I place his victory in saving De Beauvoir as one of his greatest. I am absolutely certain that if my father had not spent half his life, for free, fighting to save this area then it would not be standing today.

...

There were two strands to Graham the architect. Firstly, as a journalist with the *Architects' Journal* and *The Architectural Review*. The knowledge he had of design, implementation, planning law, building regulations and the machinations of local government meant he had a unique authority – the practical knowledge to challenge Hackney Council on every detail of every proposal. How they must have hated it!

The other side to his career was in building appraisal. When he died in 2011, messages came through from all around the world from some of the most eminent architecture and design practices – from the USA, Canada, China, Australia, Singapore, Italy, Spain, The Netherlands, and from the head of RIBA in the UK with whom he had worked for more than 20 years – praising him and his method of appraising buildings, a method which is still in use today. On some of the biggest landmark developments like The Gherkin, Broadgate, Stockley Park, and many others, you can see my father's colourful hand-sketched analyses showing recommendations and revisions. He personally advised British Telecom on their portfolio of buildings in the UK. Such was the esteem that he was held in his profession.

This was the expertise that walked into a local community meeting organised by Stuart Weir in 1968. The two immediately became friends and a council accustomed to issuing policy with barely a murmur to a placid community suddenly had to contend with two young, ferociously talented and dynamic individuals at the beginning of their careers. To be honest, I don't think Hackney Council would have known what hit them. My father realised that goodwill alone was not going to win this argument, and that without him the campaign would fail; he felt compelled to get involved despite having a young family. How fortunate for De Beauvoir that he did! He added the professional clout of someone who really was an expert in his field, the one person who could talk directly to planners because he was one.

...

With De Beauvoir the clue is in the name – 'beautiful view'. Graham fell in love with it architecturally so there was no way he was going to allow its destruction. It became his project. The *De Beaver* newspaper – and boy, did they beaver away – became the mouthpiece of the campaign and Graham had a way of harnessing the power of the local community with inclusive events and fundraisers. Everyone had a role and brought talents that were intrinsic to its success. My mother Jo Parsey was responsible for the sponsorship and advertising. She raised £3000 from local businesses, which was an enormous amount. I never knew that when I was running around posting newspapers through letterboxes with my brother and sister that I was saving the area!

...

Back then Hackney was a borough down on its knees, mentioned in news stories almost exclusively in terms of its poverty, urban decay and social deprivation. You spat the word Hackney out of your mouth. In our immediate locality every second house had corrugated iron fences instead of railings. It was common to see windows boarded up, derelict houses, squatted houses, buildings where the top floors were not lived in because of leaking roofs. As children we ran through people's gardens like they were adventure playgrounds, because there were broken walls between houses. Rag and bone horse drawn carts came once a week trading junk. Public baths served people without hot water. Eddie the paraffin man had a regular circuit and some houses still had gas lighting.

Yet this dour backdrop had its own colour. The characters, mixture of people and community was

Advert for De Beauvoir Association fundraising event. 1972

tangible and intoxicating – West Indian, Pakistani, Irish, and Londoners (remember them?). The noise and smells of home cooking was a delight, so too was Ridley Road market, the MOT testing bays, the buzz of woodsaws from the last remaining piano factories, the last of the East End wideboys and gangsters driving impeccable primrose yellow Jaguars, and the Four Aces club that hosted proper reggae music. The polyphony of real life happening in front of your eyes made it a wonderful area to grow up in.

I think the resistance of local people to the destruction of De Beauvoir was the first episode in Hackney finding pride in itself – saying no to collective low self-esteem and resisting rule from above; that local people might have a greater wisdom than the perceived authority.

...

We sold the family house when my father died and I half regret not asking the new owner to put a little blue plaque up for him. I do think he deserves it. He sacrificed a great deal of his time to support normal local people and improve their lives with no advantage to himself, writing letters, holding surgeries for the General Improvement Area, providing an alternative to the wholesale demolition of the area through patient conservation and the implementation of his own vision. Then having to present this all to a stubborn, reluctant, cash strapped council to reverse its policy and back him instead. It was a hell of a lot of work.

He completed house-to-house surveys and called in architecture students for others. It's an enormous task if you consider it, to survey an entire area consisting of hundreds of properties, but that way he was able to counter the council's surveyors, who ran around condemning houses on sight without even being given access by residents. Meanwhile, Graham knocked on doors, chatted with people in their homes over a cup of tea, did a survey, then moved on to the next house. A genius of simple direct action.

Graham always took the long view. He makes us reflect on the nature of altruism, voluntary work, charity and community. His definition of an architect was someone who made a massive and meaningful contribution to his immediate environment. It should make us think about what is important in life and what a meaningful life is.

Downham Road, south side. c.1968

ABEL ESIEN and *GRACE ESIEN*

I was born in Nigeria. I came in 1957 and my wife came in 1964. I didn't get anyone's money to come here. We came here after Nigeria became independent, as commonwealth students. I came to study law at Manchester University. I was there until 1960, and then I came to London. When I came here I had to work. The very first day in London, I took up washing the lions in Trafalgar Square. It was a good life. I lived quietly. That was '62, '63.

I came to London to concentrate on the bar final. I finished part one. The final, I passed, but the corrupt secretary failed me because he wanted money. I didn't have money to give him. A South African man. I was actually given my papers to expect my call to the bar. Bar final part two in those days, and maybe still now: you have not passed until you have been published in *The Times*. Waiting for Friday, I got *The Times* when it was published. I looked through it all and my name wasn't there. I appealed and he said, 'why did you take too long to appeal?', and they refused. I didn't know that apartheidism was strongly entrenched in the councils in Gray's Inn by that South African.

It was during that period that Mandela was seeking support. By then I wanted to stay because I had a family. That was why I turned to science.

…

You cannot get any change in isolation. In one place, as it is here, people come in with ideas from other places. They get their demands and go to the council: 'we want that, we want this'. But the major change will come from the Church. The Church is intertwined with the life of De Beauvoir. Whenever change comes, it comes first from the Church.

I can't think of any new establishment here that would attract people in the same way. If you examine the religiosity of the people, their desire to be true Christians, or true Anglicans, or even if you are not a Christian, say, you are not an aggressive atheist, we can live together in peace, we can still grow firmly and amicably. It is the religion that controls the area – that matters. The binding factor that keeps people here: St Peter De Beauvoir.

...

Ufton Road, there is a small park by the side. They use it for tennis, or for some games. That space could be used for a building, because it serves no purpose. If they want to do some practice, they have so many other spaces to do it, and leave that space for a building we can accommodate.

Some years ago, when I was the chairman of the Tenants and Residents Association here, we guarded the open spaces on the estate when the council wanted to take them up. I think they wanted them for sports – always, they wanted it for sports – and we suggested just an open space where people can sit down for a few moments. The idea of putting a permanent building there didn't come into our minds, but that would have been a very good idea. We had good debates when I was chairman. We used to go on tour and hire coaches, to go for one or two days outside London. We had some training for management and to manage the funds, especially.

We had to get involved with the Residents Association. I might want a lift and I may not have to go to the council straight. So I put it through the Residents Association, and they put it through. You know this pyramid?

Quarrelling came in, and the council were finding faults with their own method. People who had the authority were saying they did not recognise us; it must pass through certain stages, which they prescribe. By that time, I got fed up.

That lift could be out of order for 6 months. What can you do? Why go to a meeting? What are they going to tell you? Nothing. It was not an easy job to bring up a family in this building for him. And for me – God no.

...

I've been here since 1971, from Stoke Newington. My wife wouldn't like to remember it there. We had one room, you share your kitchen, and then, the worst thing is, if you have a visitor, the landlord will want to snoop. Electricity; he will say, 'don't turn your light on'. That petty way of life – it can't be tolerated at all. The private landlord makes your life intolerable. You want to leave your house to your studies. By the time you come back, somebody has already come to check.

He managed to arrange my eviction and it went to the court.

The landlord beat me. We had to go to the tribunal to get the rent. It wasn't a good house. I was pregnant. I can't forget.

The council was waiting to see when we would be pulled out and put on the road, so then they could give us a place. Wonderful procedure!

That's why we moved here. The people at the tribunal gave us a place.

They've pulled that place down now and built council flats. He never had many tenants.

...

Old De Beauvoir did not come up at all when I was chairman, not at all. Discussion in those days centred on the use of the open spaces, the canal walk, and looking after repairs. Those are the things we were concerned with.

The people living around the square sent out the periodical every three months or so. It's called *De Beaver*. It's good news. It went round to discuss some old houses and inhabitants and so on. But we never imbibed that in what we represented here, on this estate.

NOTICE TO ALL TENANTS

A PROTEST MEETING FOR TENANTS
IS TO BE HELD ON THURS. NEXT
<u>23rd May</u> AT 4-30. P.M. ON THE
GREEN AT THE REAR OF ROZEL CRT.
(if wet <u>the hut will be used</u>).

THIS IS AN OPEN MEETING ~~FOR~~
HELD IN THE INTEREST OF
ALL TENANTS. YOUNG & OLD
TO PROTEST AGAINST THE ROAD
CONDITIONS & EXTRA HEAVY
TRAFFIC USING DOWNHAM &
DE-BEAUVOIR RD, DURING THE
SIX MONTHS EXPERIMENTAL
RD CLOSURES. ALL TENANTS
WILL BE GIVEN THE CHANCE
TO SPEAK FREELY. MEMBERS
OF HACKNEY COUNCIL LOCAL
COUNCILLORS AND PRESS WILL
BE INVITED.
    IT IS MOST IMPORTANT THAT
WE HAVE A GOOD TURNOUT, AS
THE FUTURE OUTLOOK ON CLOSURES
    CONCERNS ALL RESIDENTS.

UFTON COMMUNITY CENTRE

12 UFTON ROAD
LONDON N1

01-254 2941

SUMMER PROGRAMME 1986

Buses: 22, 22A to
Kingsland High St Fire Station
left into Downham Road
76, 141 to Southgate Rd
Right into Downham Road
277,38,30 to Southgate
Rd. left into Southgate Rd. 10 Minute walk

The Ufton Community Centre is open 6 days a week, and provides workshops in golf, thi-chia, transcendental meditation, drama ect, and runs many activities including a pensioners lunch club, youth club, disco's and entertainments, and classes. Many of these activities are free, the rest are very inexpensive with special rates for the unemployed and pensioners. The centre also runs holiday playschemes during the Easter and Summer holidays, and arranges outings for users of the centre. The range of activities are expanding all the time, and any member of the community is welcome.

TRIP	£4	HARLEM DANCE THEATRE	Thurs 10th July	6.00 pm
THEATRE	£2	BUBBLE THEATRE	Sat 12th July	7.30 pm
	£1	CAN'T PAY WON'T PAY		
EVENT	free	FETE AND OPEN DAY	Sat 26th July	11.00 am
YOUTH	50p	CARNIVAL QUEEN & ESCORT SELECTION DISCO	Sat 26th July	7.00 pm
KIDS	15p day £2	PLAYSCHEME for four weeks Drop in an pick up a playscheme programme	Mon 28th July Fri 22nd August	10.30 am 4.40 pm
SOCIAL	free	MULTI RACIAL OPEN EVENING	Wed 30th July	7.00 pm
TRIP	small charge	MUMS AND TODDLERS MYSTERY PICNIC TRIP	Fri 1st August	11.00 am to 7.00 pm
TRIP	small charge	SEASIDE TRIP	Fri 15th August	10.00am to 7.00pm
EVENT	free	DE BEAUVOIR CARNIVAL	Sat 30th August	11.00 am
YOUTH	50p	ROLLER DISCO	Sat 30th August	7.00 pm
YOUTH		AUTUMN YOUTH CLUB PROGRAMME STARTS	Mon 6th Sept	7.00 pm
ADULT EDUCATION INSTITUTE	£1	BLACK STUDIES	Wed 2/9/16/23 July	7.50pm
SHORT SUMMER PROGRAMMES	£1	KNOW YOUR ROOTS - LEARN ABOUT YOUR NEIGHBOUR CULTURAL COOKERY AFRICAN & CARIBBEAN COOKERY	Fri 11th July Wed 2/9/16/23 July	7.50pm
SOCIAL	free	LIVING IN A MULTI RACIAL SOCIETY, INFORMAL DISCUSSION LED BY NEVILLE BRAITHWAITE	Wed 30th July	7.00 pm

Phone Barryter Brigette on 254-2941 for details of these and all our regular activities ESPECIALLY if you would like to start or participate in a new one.

ROGER WARD

I moved into De Beauvoir in the 1970s when it was already a conservation area and I still knew very little about the Ufton Centre in the 1980s when I was asked to be its chairman. My memories are hazy, but I guess I was approached by Rev Andy Windross, of St Peter's church, the only director of the Centre I knew. My contribution was to read the monthly papers produced by Tina Steggles, the bookkeeper, and run the monthly meeting. It was a community centre, where local people could drop in, and which afforded space for various activities. I was not involved on a day-to-day basis, but Eric Newman, another director who lived and worked nearby, took a lively interest in it. Indeed, we were a lively, motivated bunch of directors.

The first challenge was to replace the centre manager who had resigned, which we did. But the centre was not thriving and I co-opted Stephen Hazell Smith, a local accountant, to the board to supervise the finances. The second challenge was building maintenance. The centre had been converted from an old factory and was showing signs of dilapidation. Serious remedial work was needed to attract more users. I believe we contacted Hackney Leisure Services for financial support at that time but had no success. We then recruited a professional fundraiser Eric knew, but a few months later she had drawn a blank too. Then, at one of our meetings, Stephen produced a letter from Robson Rhodes, our auditors, stating that the centre was working at a loss and unless they had a satisfactory answer to how we could extinguish the deficit, the directors would be personally liable for the losses. This was before any building work, and was obviously extremely critical. Matters had come to a head.

The directors arranged an urgent meeting with Hackney Leisure Services at the Town Hall one evening to explain the position and seek their help. Their representative turned our plea for financing down. However, he told us how valuable the amenity was, and how sincerely they wanted it to continue and gave us a verbal undertaking that the directors' losses would be made good in time. This did not satisfy us and it was not going to satisfy Robson Rhodes, so we asked him to commit this offer to paper but he refused. This was too vague to be acceptable and placed the directors in an impossible position. Sadly we decided to close the Centre, while informing Leisure Services immediately in the hope they would reopen it. They never did. I vividly recall us padlocking the front door. I suspect Hackney had overspent on the Britannia Centre, and the Ufton Centre land had alternative uses. I guess my association with the Ufton Factory Organisation lasted no more than a year.

...

De Beauvoir was very different in the 1970s when we arrived to what it is today. The square was bare. A JCB stood in the middle which children played on. Several of the houses were empty, some being refurbished, some frontages were of corrugated iron. Our house had been empty for three years at least.

Gentrification might have been sweeping Canonbury but had not reached De Beauvoir. Within days of moving in we were burgled. The intruder was so shocked to find people in bed in an apparently derelict house he shot downstairs and escaped out of the back window, abandoning his ladder. A squad car arrived within minutes. Even in the 1990s a policeman asked me 'what sort of idiot parks an Aston Martin in De Beauvoir?'. (It was not me.)

...

I did not know Graham Parsey, but I am very familiar with his name as a key proponent of the De Beauvoir conservation area, and without whose efforts much of the neighbourhood would have disappeared under the Hackney council bulldozers. The character of the area owes much to him and to the others who campaigned alongside him.

A guide to WELFARE SERVICES AND BENEFITS for families, old people, mothers and children, the handicapped, disabled and blind, low wage-earners, fatherless families, and tenants.

WELFARE
& YOU

Please look through this simple guide to services and benefits you are entitled to, and put a √ by those you need or would like more information about. Then fill in your name and address on the back, and send the leaflet back to us (please see back cover for details).

For further full and quick information, a welfare worker from Hackney Welfare Department will be specially at the De Beauvoir Association advice centre in the crypt of St. Peters Church, in Northchurch Road, at these times this week:

Thursday, January 15th from 10 a.m. to 9 p.m.
(Please note evening extension).

Friday, January 16th from 10 a.m. to 4.30 p.m.

Saturday, January 17th from 10 a.m. to 12 noon.

Please use this special advisory service. It is for your benefit.

ROBIN SIMPSON

I'd had two previous jobs before Centerprise. One was working for the Child Action Poverty Group, as what we would today call a welfare rights advisor, and the other was for the Manor Road Youth & Community Centre, where I organised youth clubs on-site. The post then became vacant at Centerprise.

Centerprise was a café, bookshop, publishing project, reading centre, youth club, crèche, performance space, meeting room provider and advice centre, all in one building. An American called Glenn Thompson set it up in the early 1970s, modelling it on similar places in the USA. It was a collective in terms of its internal work structure, with a committee of management, but I think we can overdo the collective rhetoric. The vast majority of the work that I did was person-to-person – individual and often confidential.

A common reason for somebody to be facing eviction from her house – and it was usually a woman – was that the husband had walked out. That's not the kind of stuff that you take collective action about. A lot required really quite delicate and confidential advice. Whatever high-minded collective resolutions were made by our committee of management, the fact is, to execute the actual action on behalf of individual people, you had to deal with them as they came through the door. If all you do is concentrate on the collective and forget the individual, you end up with some very crude solutions.

...

I was so busy with the advice work that it was hard to get too involved in the more political activities. I was a member of the Labour Party, but not a very active one. In fact, the problem in that respect was that it was often the Labour council that we were arguing against, because of their very old-fashioned attitudes to conservation and their really very casual attitudes to eviction policy.

A lot of the time the actions were appeals at social security tribunals, because people's benefit was incorrectly calculated, or they were refused particular allowances they were entitled to – for example, to buy a new cooker or a new bed. These were discretionary benefits and so, if the discretion had been used to refuse them, they had the right of appeal, and I was the person that would take cases to individual tribunals.

What really brought me to the fore in terms of housing was the 1972 Housing Finance Act. It introduced housing benefit for the first time, which was a social security benefit administered by local housing authorities. The calculations involved were extremely complex and, as I subsequently discovered, Hackney Council were making a real mess of administering it.

Just after I left Centerprise, I discovered from leaked papers that the vast majority of elderly tenants being evicted by the council at that time were victims of housing benefit miscalculations – 31 from a total of 32. The council had systematically underestimated their housing benefit. I leaked this to *The Guardian* with the co-operation of Stuart Weir and others, and it got an article in their centre pages. By gradually 'dripping on a stone' like this, we did alter council policy – they became much more systematic in the way they evaluated people's entitlements.

We had very few failures. We nearly always won. Centerprise became known as a place that you could go to if you needed help, and that was true. People did come through the door absolutely desperate, and we were nearly always able to make some reasonably sensible suggestion.

...

When we moved into the road we live on, a friend counted 30 empty houses on our street. All over Hackney, there were huge numbers of empty houses. A lot were squatted. The population had plummeted. It had been, I think, over 200,000. It was down, in the 1961 or '71 census, to 160,000. I think it's now back up to something like a quarter of a million.

The Greater London Council was a housing authority in those days and many of the GLC estates were in the outskirts of London. So, for many 'East Enders', the dream was to get a nice council house in Woodford, and good luck to them – many of them took that. There was a drive towards the outer suburbs for perfectly normal reasons.

Hackney culture very much followed the idea of 'homes for the heroes', the argument that the workers deserved decent housing, which of course was true. The problem was that the Labour councils were so set in their ways that their idea of progress was to flatten anything old, and replace it with council housing.

Demolition was an absolute scourge, because the time from a demolition order going on a property – or a council resolution to demolish a whole street – to the first tenants moving in could be ten years. Ten years is enough time to blight the life of a child. The people who lived in those streets during that time were just living in utter misery, because no-one's going to spend money on a house which is about to be demolished. Many families just moved out rather than put up with these deteriorating conditions.

Hackney used Compulsory Purchase Orders to buy whole swathes of the borough and then sit on them and do nothing. The housing department was so huge that it couldn't possibly keep tabs on all these different houses that it was purchasing to either renovate or demolish, and so the process used to take forever. People would spend a decade living with scenes of utter devastation around them.

So it was a good thing that there was a tendency towards restoration and improvement as opposed to demolition, but the council tended not to do that very well either. In fits of madness, they would acquire whole properties just because they were available. Houses were relatively cheap because you couldn't get a mortgage in Hackney, so it was easy for the council to buy them, but they lacked the wherewithal to actually do them up properly. The house opposite us was bought by the council and stayed empty for years. It was then renovated but the plumber left the tap on one winter. The water ran all year, all through the winter. The ceiling collapsed and so it all had to be done all over again.

...

The summer holidays were a nightmare for parents. If parents were working, primary school children were effectively left unsupervised and could get up to all sorts of mischief. There was very little provision for them. There were two kinds of projects that I set up in both Manor Road and at Centerprise. There were dedicated playground schemes in open spaces. There were also teaching schemes. Teachers were very badly paid – many were very young, and they were very happy to spend three weeks in the summer doing supplementary classes and play activities for kids, which also took place largely in the playgrounds. There were also lots of outings; the Inner London Education Authority were fantastic in providing us with buses to take these kids to various places around London. I'm very proud of this, because they worked really well.

...

The interesting thing about De Beauvoir Town is that it was still very much an artisan class community held together by leaseholds. The problem was in those days, anyone that raised questions about the wisdom of demolishing buildings which were beautiful and could be made into very decent housing was systematically denigrated as a middle-class do-gooder.

I remember once there was a debate in the council about improvement grants that private landlords could apply for, and quite right – why exclude them? If it brings benefits to their tenants, why shouldn't they be eligible? Stuart Weir – his name was so slandered – put forward a proposal which would make it more cost-effective for a landlord who lived on the premises to divide the rest of the house into two separate tenancies, because many of the houses in De Beauvoir Town were very big, and it was quite possible to create three units out of one house. When Stuart was later on the shortlist to be the Labour Party candidate for MP – and came very close to getting it – his opponents put the word around that 'Stuart Weir is a friend of the private landlord'. This, after all the years he'd campaigned to improve housing conditions, council housing and private rented housing, and providing social housing in De Beauvoir through a local trust.

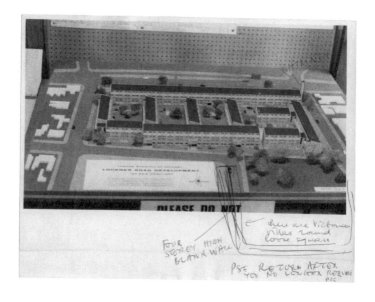

FOUR STOREY HIGH
BLANK WALL

there are Victorian
villas round
loose square

PSE RETURN AFTER
YOU NO LONGER REQUIRE
PIC

APPENDICES

AFTERWORD

Over the past six or seven years, I've been involved with a few different groups in east London that are all concerned with spatial justice in one way or another. Within this wider area, my immediate neighbourhood of De Beauvoir Town is an anomaly. If you exclude its post-war housing estates, its property is of the lowest density and highest value in the borough. In the decade I've lived in the neighbourhood, it has seemed that what is collectively possible within it is delimited, in part, by what it is understood to be; the narratives of it, circulating in it, and manifest in the area itself, in the stuff of it.

This is the problem, political and aesthetic, that initiated the work that led to this publication. It has prompted performances, discussion events, introductions, conversations and formal interviews. It led to the disclosure of hundreds of images and documents not previously in public space, and their redistribution to public and independent archive institutions. This was all an end in itself – the purpose of pursuing the problem, at least as much as making this publication: intervening in the problem as a means of interrogating it. As such, if this work is of consequence, it is likely to originate in the period before publication, as much as after.

I knew at the outset that De Beauvoir Town had begun as a 'garden square' masterplanned area in the early 19th century, and that this masterplan was aborted mid-completion, making for a common, longstanding identity as both self-contained and one of a kind. This is a combination that has attracted successive generations of the middle classes for most of the period since.

Now I know that this masterplan came at the very end of the garden square movement, but it also came at the height of a wave, in Europe, North America and elsewhere, of so-called 'utopian communities'. An important figure in this movement is Robert Owen, familiar to schoolchildren as the 'enlightened' mill-owner of New Lanarkshire. At the time the De Beauvoir layout was being drawn up, Owen was speaking regularly just down the road at the London Tavern on Bishopsgate, promoting his own plan for a masterplanned, model settlement.

Owen's proposal, and others from the period, bear a superficial resemblance to the De Beauvoir plan, perhaps reflecting a common classical influence: a radially divided square with open, green spaces, particularly at the centre, all interspersed with housing and public buildings. The plan was instantly, widely criticised. The then-famous Radical William Cobbett argued that it betrayed a coercive, paternalistic conception of 'community' and refused residents' own intellectual and political liberty.

I don't know of any concrete, contemporary connection between the Owen and De Beauvoir plans, and there are plenty of reasons to believe they have entirely parallel histories. For one, the premise of Owen's plan was to house the poor. This was never the case in De Beauvoir; the earliest housing was built less lavishly than the bulk that followed after the original plan was abandoned, but it was never intended for labourers. There is probably little to be read into the neat coincidence of Owen's brief run of public speaking in London with the planning of De Beauvoir Town. On the other hand, it doesn't seem a coincidence that 'community' was spatialised so similarly in these plans, and in so many others, realised and not. That has been enough to make me wonder about their relationship to me, and to this publication, as well.

As I said before, the problem this publication came from took 'De Beauvoir Town' as a premise – naturalised and generative – from day one. I was aware of that, of course, but I knew the recent collective action that interested me so much had done so as well. That had made sense, in turn, because De Beauvoir was the area identified by the local authority for wholesale demolition. It is also the area that people affected apparently identified as their neighbourhood, and this long-established, common identification seems to have done a lot for the campaign.

In sum, historical and self awareness aren't necessarily enough to evade the imperative to think of the area as self-contained and singular. Perhaps there would be no cause to want to if it was of no consequence, but I worry that it helps to elicit a narrative of greater autonomy than is deserved. The spaces of De Beauvoir were produced with wealth and resources gathered from elsewhere, with varying degrees of coercion, be it via the East India Company in the 18th century, or via central government in the 20th. This publication is an investigation of this imperative, but it is a symptom of it, as well.

IMAGE SOURCES

The images in this publication come from personal collections discovered, loaned and donated over the course of research, as well as material deposited with state archives. The key below details these sources, so that they may be referenced against each of the images in the lists that follow.

KEY

The abbreviations refer to the image source. Where that source is a personal collection, a number follows the abbreviation if the image author is atypical for that collection.

Some images are individually authored and some collectively, by a conventional understanding of those terms. Individual authors are credited only where it has been verifiable. In instances where authorship is collective and uncredited and it hasn't been possible to confirm the individuals responsible, the name of the organisation (that is, the collective author) is given. Where the source is an institutional archive, the number denotes the reference code used by that institution.

Other images were produced for this publication. Some approximate existing images that were not used for copyright or artistic reasons.

DBA   The current-day De Beauvoir Association, formed 2004. Authors: (1) The De Beauvoir Association, formed 1968; (2) Ufton Factory

Organisation. At the time of writing, all of the *De Beaver* newsletters are available to read in full on the De Beauvoir Association website at http://www.debeauvoir.org.uk/debeaver.html

HA   Hackney Archives. Ref: (1) P4810
      (2) D/F/TYS/59/3; (3) P4835; (4) Hackney Gazette;
      (5) D/B/HPP; (6) P14458.94; (7) P2399;
      (8) H/E/165.

BRO   Berkshire Record Office. Ref: (1) D/EBY/P86;
      (2) D/EBy/L21/1-14.

GP   The estate of Graham Parsey. Author: Graham
      Parsey. Exceptions: (1) De Beauvoir Trust;
      (2) Hackney London Borough Department of
      Architecture and Planning;
      (3) The De Beauvoir Association, formed 1968;
      (4) author unknown.

GR   Original image, Graham Reid.

GRE   Greenwood's map of London, 1826. Author:
      Mark Annand. Host: Bath Spa University.

JH   Original image, Jonathan Hoskins.

TNA   The National Archives. Ref: HLG 118/73.

SW   The collection of Stuart Weir. Author: Stuart
      Weir. Exceptions: (1) The De Beauvoir
      Association, formed 1968; (2) Ideal Standard
      Ltd; (3) De Beauvoir Association Southern Area
      Action Group; (4) author unknown.

WEL   Weller's map of London, 1868.

Image sources are listed in order of journal entry, and in the order they appear within each entry. Where all images in an entry are from the same source, that source is given only once.

4th June 2005	GR
7th June 2005	GP, GR, HA (1)
[Inserted page]	HA (2), WEL, GRE
8th June 2005	GP
10th June 2005	GP
7th July 2005	GR
14th July 2005	GR
[Inserted page]	DBA (1)
[Inserted page]	DBA (1)
[Inserted page]	DBA (1)
15th August 2005	GP
21st August 2005	HA (3)
10th September 2005	HA (1), BRO (1)
[Inserted page]	SW
17th September 2005	SW
22nd September 2005	GP
[Inserted page]	SW
8th October 2005	GP
9th October 2005	GP
11th October 2005	SW
14th October 2005	GP
15th October 2005	GP, GP (1)
[Inserted page]	GP
23rd October 2005	GP
27th October 2005	HA (4)
30th October 2005	GP

31st October 2005	GP (2)
2nd November 2005	GP
4th November 2005	GP
10th November 2005	SW (1), SW (2), HA (4), DBA (1)
[Inserted page]	GP
17th November 2005	GP, DBA (1)
[Inserted page]	JH
8th December 2005	GP
12th December 2005	GP
13th December 2005	GP, GP, HA (5)
25th December 2005	GP
2nd January 2006	GP, GP, DBA (2), JH, JH, SW (3)
6th January 2006	HA (2), SW
7th January 2006	SW, GR, GR, HA (6)
8th January 2006	GP
17th January 2006	GP
2nd February 2006	GP
5th February 2006	GP, GP, DBA (1), GP
15th February 2006	HA (7)
27th February 2006	HA (8), GR
1st March 2006	GP
2nd March 2006	DBA (1), GP
5th July 2006	TNA
9th July 2006	TNA
14th July 2006	TNA

RELATED ACCOUNTS

Images are referenced by page number.

203	GP (4)
206	SW (1)

209	SW (1)
212	SW (3)
215	SW (4)
218	SW (1)
222	SW (4)
232	HA (2)
235	BRO (2)
240	SW (4)
250	GP (4)
255	GP (4)
260	JH
265	DBA (2)
266	GP
271	GP (3)
274	SW
279	SW (4)
280	DBA (2)
284	SW (1)
291	GP (4)
COVER	GP

ACKNOWLEDGEMENTS

This publication came about over two years of public and private discussion, contributions of images, documents and other material, introductions, interviews and critical feedback. All of the following people were part of this process and their generous contributions are greatly appreciated:

Sam Ashenden, Edward Benyon, Paul Bolding, Mike Brooks, James Brown, Anna Colin, Fiona Darbyshire, Matthew De Kersaint Giraudeau, Stefan Dickers, Graham Downes, Michael Edwards, Abel Esien, Grace Esien, Dorothy Esien, Chris Fite-Wassilak, Andrea Francke, Teresa Gleadowe, Elizabeth Haines, Jeremy Hornsby, Jay Hornsby, Jen Hoyer, Jack James, Ross Jardine, Chris Jones, Brandon LaBelle, Carol Lee, Colin Lindley, Josh MacPhee, Hilary Mandleberg, Greg Mihalko, Joan Miller, Laura Mitchison, Siân Mogridge, Deepa Naik, Kirsty Norman, Trenton Oldfield, Hayden Parsey, Martha Parsey, Joanna Peace, Julia Porter, Michael Rank, Ester Rank, Alan Rayner, Jane Rolo, Eva Rowson, Dominic Simpson, Robin Simpson, Laurence Taylor, Lesley Thompson, Rosa Vilbr, Roger Ward, Stuart Weir, Ken Worpole, Susannah Worth, Robin Young and Lailan Young.

Special thanks are extended to Hayden and Martha Parsey, who are the executors of the estate of their late father, Graham Parsey. Around half of the images in this publication are from this collection, and all were contributed for no fee, and allowing complete artistic control of their use within this publication.

COLOPHON

Own De Beauvoir!
by Jonathan Hoskins

Commissioned and supported by Open School East,
London 2014–2016

Design:
Luke Gould

Printing:
Die Keure

Proofreading:
Susannah Worth

Original images:
Graham Reid

Additional writing:
Dominic Simpson

ISBN 978-1-5262-0631-2

Contact: dbjonathanhoskins@gmail.com